REPORT WRITING IN PSYCHOLOGY AND PSYCHIATRY

REPORT WRITING IN PSYCHOLOGY AND PSYCHIATRY

JACK T. HUBER

HARPER & ROW, Publishers
New York, Evanston and London

A-M

Library of Congress catalog card number: 61–10682

CONTENTS

PREFACE

If the pages of report writing in psychology, psychiatry, and related professions were laid end to end they would easily reach from New York to Lord knows where. Many people feel that our reports could be a lot better—could be written with greater skill, could better communicate what the writer intended, could better meet the needs of the reader, and could be more of a pleasure to read. Endless hours of anxiety (of students) and displeasure (of students and professionals) are spent in writing them. This, too, could be different. If students are instructed well, they can find great interest and pleasure in report writing.

We spend countless hours teaching graduate psychology students and psychiatric residents how to interview, how to administer and interpret tests, and how to do therapy. All of these enterprises end up on paper in the form of a report. And yet there is little or no training given on how to write the report.

I have long been interested in a "how-to-do-it" book on report writing, mostly because I have always enjoyed writing reports and because I believe such a book is needed. I have written reports for psychiatric hospitals, child guidance clinics, Army rehabilitation centers, psychological consulting firms for industry, private psychotherapists, and out-patient clinics. In each setting and in each case I found totally different problems and, at the same time, numerous common elements. These likenesses and differences are what I have tried to show in this manual.

I might have begun the book with long discussions of testing, interviewing, interpretation of behavior, theories of personality—all of which are background for writing a report about an individual. None of these appears here. Many volumes have been written on all these subjects; furthermore, they constitute the major subject matter in training programs in psychology and psychiatry.

This manual is solely concerned with writing reports. In order to write a report, you must first have the right kinds of data and some notions about what a report is. Then, for most purposes, you must formulate the case. These are the initial topics of the manual. Following these topics are some outlines for various kinds of reports and then some comments on the specific problems encountered in this kind of writing. I have also included two neglected topics in our professions—therapy progress recording, which is a form of report writing, and confidentiality, which is crucial to what is included in a report. Some examples of reports written by psychologists and psychiatrists who have been writing reports for many years appear at the end of the book. I have attempted to relate the points made in the manual to these quoted reports by commenting on each report. These are the contents of the manual.

The point of view of this book is this: A report contains what one human being has to say about another human being. We cannot escape this fact. Because of their personal nature, therefore, reports cannot or should not be written in the same way by every writer. I have proposed numerous outlines in order that the reader may find an outline which is best for him. I believe there are some specific rules about report writing, and I have included them. I also believe that there are some basic considerations, some theoretical issues, which should be considered by report writers. These are discussed at the beginning of the book.

This manual is written primarily for students and professionals in psychiatry and psychology. Both professions are included because of the similarity in the kinds of reports required in both. I also feel each can learn by examining the kinds of outlines used by the other profession. I believe it may also be of some value to personnel workers, speech therapists, reading specialists, and others who must produce reports on individuals. It may be used as a text or reference book. However it is used, I hope it will help the reader produce with more ease and pleasure reports which are easy and pleasurable to read, which meet the needs of the reader, and which communicate what the reporter intended to communicate.

I wish to thank the following friends for their kindness in reading and criticizing my manuscript: Jacob Cohen, Ph.D., Shirley S. Cohen, Gordon F. Derner, Ph.D., R. E. Escovado, Samuel P. Oast, M.D., John J. Vetter, M.D., and Winifred S. Vetter, M.S.W. To Mrs. Alfred Treiber, my secretary at Adelphi College for the last four years, go my sincere thanks for her sustained interest and efficiency.

I am also grateful to the psychological consulting firms of Richardson, Bellows, Henry, and Company, and Rohrer, Hibler, and Replogle for permission to quote their material. To Dr. Karl A. Menninger go my thanks for the use of material reprinted by permission from his book, *A Manual for Psychiatric Case Study*, Grune & Stratton, 1952. To the publishers who allowed me to quote from their publications I am pleased to list their books.

Perhaps my greatest debt of gratitude I owe to my students

in the Ph.D. program in clinical psychology at Adelphi College, to the many psychiatrists and psychologists with whom I have discussed report writing, and to my colleagues at the numerous institutions where I have written reports. From all of these people I learned what I have written in this book.

J. T. H.

New York
March 1961

REPORT WRITING IN PSYCHOLOGY AND PSYCHIATRY

I. FOUNDATIONS OF REPORT WRITING

A report about an individual begins with the observations the reporter makes. After he has collected his data, the reporter must organize it, make sense out of it. And then he must put on paper what sense he has made. Briefly stated, this is the sequence of this manual.

Before you begin organizing your data, there are some basic problems about report writing to consider. These include the function of a report, the meaning of formulating a case, what skills, knowledge, and data you need, your relationship with the patient, and a few other basic considerations which arise in writing most reports in psychology and psychiatry. These considerations are the topics of this chapter.

THE FUNCTION OF A REPORT. The function of a report is to answer questions. The first step in writing a good report is to find the right questions to ask. The problem beginning students have is that they collect a great deal of data, but they do not know what approach to take to it. That is, they do not know what questions to ask themselves about the data.

The questions for a report come from three sources:

The referring agent (the reader)
A theory of personality
An outline for the report

Without questions from each of these sources, the student finds difficulty in writing a report which has any meaning and order. A report based solely on a theory but with no outline is lacking in order and is apt not to serve the needs of the reader. The contributions of theory to report writing will be discussed later. A report based on an outline which does not "fit" the writer's theory will be orderly in form but jumbled in meaning. The development of an outline is the topic of a large segment of this manual. A report based on a theory and an outline which fits the theory but which does not answer the questions of the reader is oriented to the writer, not the reader. This kind of report may be brilliant in content but serves no function for the reader. A report based only on the questions of the reader but without a solid foundation of theory and the order provided by an outline is apt to be thin.

Thus a meaningful, orderly, and functional report is based on questions emanating from all three sources listed above.

Since without a reader there would be no report, I shall first discuss the contribution the reader makes to the report writer.

LEARNING FROM THE READER. If the student has some theoretical notions about personality and an outline for a report, he sometimes forgets the reader. If you overlook your reader, you are, besides preparing to write a poor report, missing out on the help the reader can give you. The first question to ask when beginning a report is:

What specifically does the reader want to know about the patient?

Usually you will have a request form from the reader. This will give you some questions. If there is no request form, talk to your reader and ask him what questions he has about the patient. What difficulties is he having with the patient? What gaps are present in his understanding the patient?

Students sometimes overlook the *presenting problem* of the patient. Knowing only this will be of great aid to you in formulating the case. The presenting problem provides you with questions around which you could base your entire report: What is there about the patient and his present situation that have caused him to seek help? What was there about his development which made him susceptible to his present stresses? Are there problems other than the presenting ones? What can bring relief to the patient? Your reader knows what specific forms these questions take. If you get them from him, your report is already on its way to being formulated.

There are numerous other aids your reader has to offer you. If there is a universal reason for discouragement about report writing, it is that we too often do not know what happens to our reports. There is a simple way to find out in many instances. Simply ask your reader. Ask him if your report has been useful, what you did not answer for him, what seems inaccurate to him. There is hardly a better way to improve your next report. You may completely change your attitude toward report writing when you know that your report is read, that it has some real effect on decisions about the patient, that it is accurate (or even that it is not), that you can check your report with new data, that it will aid the therapist in working with the patient.

Apart from discovering what happens to your report and obtaining new data, you can also learn how to write better reports by learning something about the reader himself. Do your best to find out something about him. Even the briefest answers to these questions will be helpful to you:

What is his background?
What professional terms and concepts can you use and be completely understood by him?
What kind of language does he use?
What does he weight heavily?

With these questions in mind, an astute conversationalist can get the answers in a short period of time. Without this information, the writer is in the same position as the lecturer who begins his speech without knowing his audience; he knows neither what to select to say nor whether any of it will be understood.

A writer may often completely change his outlook on his reports by speaking to the reader. For example, the assumption that a speech clinician is not trained in psychoanalytic theory may be found to be completely fallacious, just as the reverse assumption may be. Similarly, psychology students may assume that readers of psychological reports understand the theory behind intelligence testing; if the reader does not, a report on intelligence may be completely misused. In industrial consulting you may learn that any mention of the word "sincerity" or "insincerity" makes your reader prick up his ears and greatly overweight the idea you are attempting to get across. Similarly, you may learn that a report without some mention of relationships with peers is no report at all to your reader.

In addition to all other advantages, you can also increase your own writing vocabulary and avoid stereotypy by talking to your reader.

Often our reader is down the hall or in a nearby clinic, but we do not "find the time" to get to know him. In any effort we make to talk to him, we have the possibility of learning a great deal about how to improve our reports. Furthermore, in learning what happens to our reports, we even stand the chance of learning to enjoy the whole process of report writing.

DO YOU NEED A THEORY OF PERSONALITY? During his internship one of my students made what was for him a major discovery: that in order to write a good clinical report one needs two things, a theory of personality and an outline for formulation. Add to this some understanding of your reader and a little writing skill and you have the tools of report writing in capsule form.

When a student hears that he must have a theory of personality, his worries begin. He may feel he does not know enough about human behavior, about theory in general, about interpretation, to face a task that requires something so complex as a theory of personality. He may rush to Freud or the theorist of his supervisor's choice. This solution, if the student does not really understand the theory he chooses, will produce reports which are sure to be disjointed and confusing. A better solution is to approach formulation with whatever you personally bring to a case. None of us is without his own "theory." "To evaluate daily events and to guide future actions, every single human being possesses a private scientific system" (Ruesch, 1951, p. 26). "There is no such thing as 'no theory.' . . . The observation of any concrete event is carried out under the dictates of some 'theory'—that is, certain things are attended to and certain things are overlooked . . ." (Hall & Lindzey, 1957, pp. 16–17). This "private scientific system" or "theory" comes from your life experiences, from your reading, and from your training. These are what you bring to a formulation.

Students wonder if they should be able to verbalize their "theory," their approach to personality. Since many experienced psychiatrists and psychologists would find it difficult to state clearly the theory they use in formulating a case, one can hardly expect students to do so. For report writing, the important consideration is that the writer have a concept of what the manifest behavior means about the patient, what ordinarily is related to or accompanies this kind of behavior, how behavior like this is learned, how the behaviors of the patient are interrelated, and how the behaviors may change. To put this another way, the writer must have some clear ideas about *observation, classification, explanation, prediction,* and *control* of human behavior. While the form of this outline is not appropriate for a report, it suggests what the writer is doing when he prepares a report about an individual. The writer chooses to observe certain phenomena and chooses to delete or overlook other phenomena, he classifies what he observes, he explains the behavior, and he makes predictions and suggestions for the control of future behavior.

In the psychological sciences we are fortunately becoming increasingly aware that we *choose* to observe and report certain behavior of a patient and choose *not* to report other behavior. You might repeatedly ask of yourself what determines your choices. Your *classification* system for ordering your statements about the behavior of a patient should be constantly reviewed to see that it is concise and that it clearly communicates what you wish to communicate. For example, does the classification of id, ego, superego really communicate clearly and succinctly the statements you wish to make? You should also be aware that your classification of a patient's behavior is not an explanation of that behavior. Labeling something is not the same as explaining it.

Your *explanations* of behavior are usually built on a current theory of personality but also often reflect your own personal life and experiences. You should be aware of the difference between the two. *Prediction* and *control* are the goals of most scientific endeavors. In report writing you should know when you can predict and when you cannot. You should also have in mind what is important to predict in any given report (e.g., success in therapy, the result of a foreseeable environmental influence on behavior). When we offer suggestions for control (e.g., what kind of therapy will produce what kinds of behavior change), our own value system is so crucially involved that we must constantly review just what it is that we consider good and bad for patients.

Some of the outlines suggested later in this manual cover *some* of these steps; I am suggesting that a good report covers *all* of them.

The student will develop and enrich his own "theory" or foundation for formulating by studiously working at it. He must continue to be aware of the implications (his assumptions, his prejudices, his own problems) of his observations, classifications, explanations, predictions, and suggestions for control of human behavior. He must approach formulation honestly with what he himself has and use only those parts of a theory which he understands. And he should increase his knowledge of human behavior by exposing himself to the complete range of theories and research now in existence.

THE OBSERVER AND THE OBSERVED. You cannot hide yourself from the reader. What comes through every report is the kind of person you are, how you feel about the patient, and what you understand about the patient.[1] Some few writers illustrate this unpleasant fact by writing in such a foggy way that the reader knows nothing about the patient and is aware only of the reporter's confusion.

As I have already stated, a report contains what one human being has to say about another human being. A report is a function of the observer, the observed, and the interaction between the two.

One way to investigate the effect of your personality on a report is to ask yourself how you feel about the patient, whether or not you like him, what things about him "rub you the wrong way." These questions are particularly appropriate

[1] The effect of the writer on his own production has been studied by various researchers. See Gage, 1951, and Robinson & Cohen, 1954.

for the student who may not have had the experience of seeing how his biases color both his writing and his interpretations. I have learned to listen carefully when a student says about a testee, "This is a really wonderful child," or "I tested a very unpleasant person yesterday," or implies in any way that he particularly liked or disliked the patient after only one meeting. A display of strong liking or disliking of a patient at the end of a one- to four-hour session is apt to reveal unusual identification, sympathy, or projection, and thus a contamination of objectivity.

This point impressed me for the first time when a student began his discussion of test results on a 6-year-old girl by telling me how "cute" and how charming the child was. He had written a report which said in essence that the child was untroubled and thus would not be a candidate for psychotherapy. In reviewing the test results together, we both became aware of the signs of trouble shown in test response after test response. The student finally concluded, "I was completely taken in." The student and I then tried a different approach to the child's charm: we questioned why the child produced this diversion and what function it served for her. My student's revised report bore little resemblance to his first try; the original would certainly have done a disservice to the child.

Another way students are apt to confuse their reports is to make value judgments of the patient without being aware that they are doing this. Judging of a patient, either in an approving or disapproving way, always warrants investigation.

In reading a report written by a student, I was struck by one sentence: "His free self-expression is delightful." The implication was that the patient's behavior "delighted" the tester. Before going over the test results, my student explained a peculiar set of circumstances. The patient's mother seemed to show a kind of sociopathic personality disturbance and the father a passive-aggressive personality. The child, my student explained, was surprisingly unscathed by the parents. Thus the child was "free" and had developed self-expression which was "delightful." My response was that if this was true, I had better reconsider some of my theoretical ideas about personality development. In going over the test results, we both noticed that every response of the child showed the effects of the parents; that in fact he was showing the early signs of personality disturbance. My student, we discovered, had very much identified with the child.

The new emphasis on countertransference in psychology and psychiatry may alert students to just such identification with patients. Students should be taught to investigate their own feelings in any contact with patients. Being aware of countertransference, they may be able to deal with it.

THE DATA FOR A REPORT. The amount of data you have available to you is a function of your profession (psychiatrist, psychologist, etc.), your role in the case, and the setting in which you work. One of the failings of students is that they do not make use of the data which *is* available.

The patient's history is the first bit of data available to most psychiatrists and psychologists. The difficulties are that students do not always get a complete history or do not use what they have. Karl Menninger (1952, pp. 42–45) has pointed out that in the new generations of psychiatrists the "art" of history taking is a dying one. Quoting Ives Hendrick of Harvard Medical School, Menninger states that we are producing a generation of clinicians with "juvenile fantasies of being sit-on-the-tail megalotherapists"; and while "fourth-year medical students do a splendid job of history-taking, . . . a comparable performance by psychiatrists under forty years of age has become a rarity." Menninger is dismayed at the "loss of accuracy and completeness of recording essentials." My own impression is that in clinical psychology the problem is just as great as it is in psychiatry.

There are at least three reasons for the present-day failure to take complete histories. One is that we have become, with the aid of psychoanalytic and other theories, very clever at making *elaborate interpretations on the basis of minimal data.* Fortunately, with the advances in the understanding of human behavior, we are often right. We begin to feel that we no longer need much of a history.

Second, we are so therapy oriented today that we have adopted a peculiar attitude toward history taking. We are taught that in interviews we should follow the *patient's leads.* We often forget that this practice emanated from the practice of psycho*therapy,* not psycho*diagnostics.* The diagnostician must investigate more than the affect-laden leads of the patient. With the great emphasis today on the patient's own perception of his problems, we have moved away from the facts of his life.

The third reason for our failure to take complete histories is our present emphasis on the *patient's feelings.* We investigate at great length the patient's feelings toward his mother, his feelings toward his siblings, his feelings toward the clinician. A report of feelings with no "facts" is a very thin report.

Thus today many reports are filled with soaring interpretations based on few data, long expositions of the patient's view of his problem (and eliminating the reporter's view), and careful consideration of the patient's (and the clinician's) "feelings." What is excluded is his history, what he has actually accomplished, how he actually behaves despite his fantasies and feelings and distortions of perception, what pressures and expectations are imposed on him by his environment, and what physical limitations restrict his activities. Many of us are familiar with the dramatic and often-cited example of the five-times-tested child who, in the hands of a thorough clinician, was found never to have been retarded, simply deaf.

Our present approaches are undoubtedly reactions against the old, flat, static fact-collecting approach. With our new emphases we are apt to end up, however, with no facts. Without facts, we write vacuous reports and do great disservice to patients.

In psychology, "blind analysis" of test results has long been decried for many reasons. We recognize that blind analysis is a "trick," it is open to vast error, there are other data available to us, and we may do real harm to the patient. However, in both psychology and psychiatry we sometimes do just this.

We may indeed be producing a group of "sit-on-the-tail megalotherapists" who use the *methods* of *psychotherapy* while the *goals* of *psychodiagnostics* are different. Our goal in diagnostics is to give meaningful information about a person, and one of our major sources of information is the history. With the advances made in psychology and psychiatry our insights are increasingly more accurate, but we need to retain the history-taking methods we have always had. We now have a great range of data—the patient's perception of his problems, his feelings (and the reporter's), the interpretations of the writer, *and* the facts of the patient's life. We need only to use what we have.

DATA FROM OTHER DISCIPLINES. Report writers have data of many kinds at their fingertips, but may neither recognize the data nor think to use them. This occurs despite the fact that today we are in a professional environment where the interdisciplinary approach is the byword of professionalism. The interdisciplinary approach arose from the gradual acknowledgment that numerous disciplines had bodies of knowledge and points of view which, if pooled, would produce an understanding of human behavior far superior to that of any single discipline. Unfortunately, the interdisciplinary approach is often only a byword. We have not extended the concept to practical usefulness; we fail to take full advantage of other disciplines. The psychologist or psychiatrist, for example, is "aware" of "sociological factors" affecting the patient's behavior, but these factors are often not investigated.

Leslie Phillips, the specialist in projective techniques, once made the statement[2] that he would not attempt to write a report about a person until he knew where the person came from. While on the surface this may appear to be a cliché, it is an unusual statement from a projective tester. In experienced hands, of course, projective tests alone provide the reporter with enough information to write an interesting report. Phillips's point is that more data is needed beyond the test responses if we want to write a *complete* report—that is, one which goes beyond intrapsychic material.

Obviously, in order fully to understand and describe a person we must have as much data as possible concerning the milieu from which the patient comes and to which he has reacted. As is pointed out elsewhere in this manual, the patient is too often conceived of as a mass of needs, conflicts, etc., almost totally unrelated to his actual environment. A good clinical report shows that the person has reacted to *something*, what that something is, and how he has reacted.

There have been times when professionals specifically avoided mentioning the environment and background of the patient. A clinician has related to me that during the early days of antidiscrimination furor, clinicians, in their effort to be beyond suspicion, deleted any reference to race, religion, or even residence area. Thus a Negro patient living amidst the pressures and complications of a poverty-stricken and crime-ridden area of Harlem was described in reports as if none of these pressures existed; they were not even mentioned.

[2] In a lecture delivered at Adelphi College.

There is a further point in Phillips's statement: we cannot predict or prognosticate unless we know and take full cognizance of the environment or "factors" to which the patient is *returning* after his hospital stay, clinic visit, or office appointment. For example, all of our hospital efforts may be in vain if our delinquent adolescent patient is doomed to return to exactly the same stressful environment from which he came to us.

Some report writers have incorporated the interdisciplinary approach into their practice and seek all kinds of data other than those data usually thought to be within the province of their own profession. These data must, of course, be (1) *pertinent* to the task of the report writer, and (2) thoroughly *understood* by him.

As to pertinence, the report writer should not collect data for its own sake, use it indiscriminately, or use it to pad or make the report appear to be more professional. Information from a medical examination, for example, that a patient is suffering from an upper respiratory infection is of doubtful importance in a report of intellectual functioning. That the patient has an uncorrected visual or hearing loss, on the other hand, is usually of crucial importance to the results of intelligence testing. Similarly, the sociological information that the patient lives in a uniquely poor block in the center of an upper socioeconomic community may have great importance in a report of his personality functioning.

If there are no social workers or sociologists on hand to investigate the environment of the patient, no physician to give a physical examination, and so on, then the clinician must collect the data he *can* collect, given his restrictions of time and knowledge. Such information is, however, becoming more and more available in many settings, though we too often do not take advantage of it. Relating to the question of *understanding* data, we do not perform our professional functioning appropriately when we make judgments and predictions on the basis of specialized data from a discipline with which we are unfamiliar. A psychologist, for example, must be cautious in the use of medical and sociological data unless he has the background to know the meaning of these data in relation to his own observations. Similarly, the psychiatrist can discuss psychological test results intelligently only if he is thoroughly conversant with the tests and theory involved.

In order to produce meaningful reports, the writer should estimate the *scope* of his reports and the available *sources of information.* He should then *select* the information which is appropriate to his report and discuss only the information about which he has thorough knowledge.

THE NORMAL AND THE PATHOLOGICAL. Leslie Phillips has pointed out[3] that the professional's interests, emphases, and approaches differ when he is dealing with the normal from when he is dealing with the pathological. When we study the pathological, our interest is in single bits of behavior, usually those which are strikingly counter to society's rules. Thus we note and discuss the suicidal attempt, the assaultive episode, or the hallucinatory experience. Our emphasis with the normal is totally different; we emphasize his *general level of functioning.* We discuss his work habits, his avocational interests, his relation with his children, etc. The essence of the difference is that we treat only the symptom-free individual as if he were a whole person. The "symptomful" patient is often treated as if he were merely a bundle of symptoms, a "thing" rather than a person.

Historically, the emphasis on symptoms can easily be explained. Psychologists and psychiatrists have always been faced with the problem of explaining symptoms and attempting to eliminate them. Because of these necessities, the report writer often restricts himself only to these issues.

[3] In his lecture at Adelphi.

I am not suggesting we eliminate the description of symptoms. Symptoms are a person's means of expressing his problems. They usually reflect his attempt at "adjustment." They are, however, only a facet of his personality. There are other factors which have operated, are presently operative, and will in the future affect his total functioning. A report on a person, whether he is "normal" or is showing pathology, should go beyond mere symptom identification. I have previously mentioned that symptoms are an important clue for beginning a report, but they are not the basis for the whole report.

The change in emphasis in psychotherapy away from total emphasis on symptoms may alter the future of psychodiagnostics and report writing. If we adapt from psychotherapy the notion of a feeling and reacting person and add to it the person's background, his environment, and the other "facts" of his life, we can produce complete reports on *people,* whether they are normal or are displaying pathology.

THE QUESTION OF DIAGNOSIS. Diagnosis presents a "question" because there are few tools in psychiatry and psychology which present so many problems and about which there are so many disagreements and misconceptions.

In preparing this manual I became involved in an illuminating survey of viewpoints on the subject of diagnosis. I canvassed senior members and students in the fields of medicine, psychiatry, and psychology. Without exception, each person evidenced strong feeling about the subject of diagnosis and gave a definite statement on the value (or lack of value) of diagnosing. There was, however, extreme variation of opinions between respondents on every point discussed.

One chief of service in a well-known mental hospital reported that all psychiatrists at his institution are required to give a diagnosis on every patient. They are also required, he added, to follow the diagnosis with a "diagnostic" statement about the patient in *operational terms.* That is to say, the patient is described in such a way that another observer could, following the description, observe the same phenomena as the reporter observed. Asked why a diagnosis was given if a description followed, the psychiatrist stated that perhaps the label really was not necessary.

Without any question, the whole subject is an extremely confused one at the present time. There are, however, two solutions. One is suggested above: describe the patient in operational terms. The other is for us to come to specific agreement on what our labels mean (to be discussed in the next section).

In the past, patients in clinics and hospitals were almost always diagnosed. Today many clinics and hospitals require a diagnosis, but many also specifically avoid it. Some clinicians are of the opinion that only the rare patient fits a diagnostic category and for this reason they refuse to pigeonhole a person into a "type." In some institutions where excellent communication provides a common understanding of existent terms, a diagnosis is a shorthand method of making some practical statements about a patient, even including, in some cases, the kind of ward to which the patient should be assigned, the range of therapies to be tried, etc.

The point is that a diagnostic label is a method of shorthand, but the meaning of symbols must be agreed upon by reporter and reader. The welfare of patients is, of course, too important to risk misunderstanding. One needs only to consider the many and varied implications of the term *schizophrenia* to appreciate the present confusion. The psychiatrist mentioned above stated that in writing a report on a patient to a physician outside his hospital, the original diagnosis of schizophrenic reaction used for this patient in the hospital was not mentioned. He reported simply that the patient was withdrawn and somewhat schizoid. Thus he used one diagnosis in his own setting, another for an outside agent.

The question, of course, hinges on communication. We would be foolish indeed to include a diagnosis in a report to someone who would not understand the diagnosis as we intend it to be understood. Diagnostic categories are, as stated previously, shorthand symbols to communicate ideas. Until the confusion is overcome, we must obviously exercise caution in the area of diagnosis.

SOME AGREEMENT ON DIAGNOSIS. The American Psychiatric Association in its diagnostic manual (1952) has done the clinical professions a service by publishing a brief code book which *could* be used by all clinicians. If we all used it, at least some of the confusion might be eliminated. While there is no agreement that it is the last word on diagnosis, it is perhaps the best diagnostic manual we have. So long as we continue to use diagnostic labels, one common source such as this will at least assure us that we are attaching commonly accepted meanings to our labels.

Two suggestions may be made about the use of the manual. The first involves the term *reaction* as used in some of the diagnoses. As the manual has developed, some of the diagnoses have moved from purely descriptive psychiatric nomenclature to categories with dynamic implications. Some of the categories are now referred to as "reactions." The distinction between "schizophrenic reaction, simple type" and "simple schizophrenia" is a sharp one. The first implies that the patient is *reacting* to something. If the reporter follows this reaction orientation, he is obliged to explain what the patient is reacting to, why he has chosen this kind of reaction, and under what circumstances the reaction might be expected to change.

The second suggestion involves assumptions. When we use the manual, our purpose is to follow a common source of definition. It is easy to follow the definition and then assume that other implications not in the definition will be taken for granted by the reader. If we do this, we are essentially back where we started. For example, we may find that a patient fits the manual's description of a diagnosis and then we assume that the diagnosis implies a specific form of treatment. My suggestion is that we must be cognizant of our assumptions. If we wish to communicate something beyond the manual's definition, we should state clearly what we wish to add to the diagnosis.

THE MAJOR THREAD. Students ask what they should first look for in the record. Schafer's statement (1954) on this question is the following:

> There is no "best way" to begin. Each record extends a different helping hand to the tester—one in an unusual score pattern, one in a dramatic image, one in a sudden change of attitude, etc. It also seems to be the case that different testers vary in what they find most helpful in a record. Once the helping hand has served its purpose, however, we must systematically explore and try to interrelate all aspects of the scores, images and test attitudes [p. 186].

While Schafer is writing about psychological tests, his point is applicable to all clinical data. His suggestion is a good one but easy for only a few reporters; it is especially difficult for the neophyte student. The task is, however, not insurmountable. The "helping hand" is seldom obvious from one reading of the record. The "major thread" usually appears if the student will read and reread the data and take notes as he reads. Since the major thread produces unity where no unity may otherwise appear, this should be the constant search of the report writer. To become aware of the thread, one may ask of the data:

> What is the one most important aspect of personality which allows this person to function as well as he is functioning at this time?

What prevents him from functioning more effectively?
What is the conflict (or problem) around which his malfunctioning revolves?

We must note one danger in centering the report around the answers to these questions. Some reports do only this, and the result is a thin statement of an idea rather than a full and complex picture of a person. The thread is only a central theme upon which to build a report.

THE WHOLE AND THE PARTS. The major thread of a person's life gives us in the briefest fashion the whole picture but it may not obviously explain the parts. From an over-all point of view there are different kinds of reports.

1. Emphasis on the *whole:* All comments revolve around a central theme, conflict, or problem, and what the patient has done to cope with it. This kind of report is appropriate if brevity is desired.

2. Emphasis on the *parts:* The report is apt to be a mass of disparate ideas with no unity. This kind of report has value where the reader is interested in particular aspects of behavior, such as in some reports for industry. There is also the danger that by not seeing the whole, any single part may be over- or underweighted and any action taken will be misguided. In industry there is a constant search for measures of such personality variables as responsibility, drive, etc. In a report on a person, we can discuss "drive" only when we see how drive is affected by and affects intellectual functioning, interpersonal relations, etc. In our search for such measures we should keep in mind that when we find them we may also find ourselves dividing a "whole person" into parts. Once we have divided him, we may never be able to put him back together again. That is, we have the parts but have lost the person.

3. Emphasis on the *whole and the parts:* In most if not all protocols we can find a central theme and many other ele-

ments, some directly related and some only scarcely related to that theme. An amalgamation of whole and parts, i.e., a report integrating the theme or themes and other elements (e.g., intellectual functioning), is obviously the most difficult and the most adequate conceptualization of the "whole person." The way to develop such an amalgamation is to formulate the case before the report is written, keeping in mind what issues need to be covered to meet the needs of the reader. Some specific methods for accomplishing this are given in the next chapter.

HOW TO BEGIN. You actually begin making a formulation while you are seeing the patient. Numerous generalizations and interpretations will come to your mind while the patient is with you. Write them down while you are testing or interviewing. Otherwise, unless you have a remarkable memory, you will forget them. Again, the minute the patient leaves, jot down your impressions. When you begin to formulate later, you will find that some of your best ideas occurred to you while in the physical presence of the patient. If you find some of your most fundamental initial impressions change while going over the data at a later time, this occurrence provides an additional provocative bit of data. The question arises, Why did I get this impression of the patient while we were together? Does he give most people this impression? What is he communicating in this "false" impression?

Regardless of the kind of outline you choose for formulation, have it before you when you are trying to put the case together. Leave a space under each heading. As you read through each patient response, ideas will occur to you. Write them down immediately under the appropriate heading. Do not trust your memory; formulating is too subtle and rapid a procedure to allow you to remember all your thoughts. If an idea is tentative, put a question mark after it.

Continue doing this until you see the central theme and its relation to all other data, in effect until you have a formulation with which you are content. My own criterion for stopping is that I can answer almost any question one might ask about the patient which relates to the original purpose of the report. And I know what questions I cannot answer with the data I have. At this point I can write a report which "hangs together," which flows, which will give the reader the feeling that he is reading about a person, not a group of disparate ideas.

Do not take *random* notes while reviewing your data. This is the hard way to get the central theme, tie your thoughts together, and prepare for writing a report. One of the functions of an outline is to give you a place to put your notes while formulating. If you use it while you are formulating, the report will come easily.

II. FORMULATING THE CASE

Up to this point, I have discussed some of the general problems of report writing—the function of a report, the sources of questions to be asked, the data of the report, and how to begin a report.

I have pointed out that the function of a report is to answer questions, and that the questions come from the reader, a theory of personality, and an outline for the report. The present chapter covers the development of an outline for the major portion of most reports in psychology and psychiatry.

Rather than refer to *the report* in this chapter, I have chosen the expression *formulating the case*. I have emphasized the formulation, rather than the actual form the report takes, for two reasons. Regardless of whether the student is orally reporting on a patient to supervisor or staff, is writing a diagnostic report, or is noting therapy progress, he must formulate the case. Secondly, while there are many special kinds of reports in psychiatry and psychology, a complete formulation of personality functioning is the basis of most reports in these professions, regardless of how much of the formulation is actually written down in any given report.

THE MEANING OF FORMULATION. One young psychiatric resident told me that when his preceptor requested him to "formulate" his first case, he did not even know what the preceptor meant. Similarly, psychology students say that when they record the IQ of a patient and are then expected to continue with statements about the patient's personality, they do not know how to go about it.

The dictionary definition of *formulate* is "to reduce to, or express in (or as in), a formula; to set forth in a definite and systematic statement." In order to develop a "definite and systematic statement," the report writer must select from what the patient has said and done, must shorten the data, and must interpret and organize it. The writer develops this statement by sifting his data through his knowledge of psychology and psychiatry, through his skill in interpretation, and through his comprehension of a chosen outline. And, fortunately or unfortunately, the sifting he does is always a reflection of his own personality. A formulation is a personal interpretation, a selection and summary, a point of view imposed on an event by the reporter.

In this manual I am restricting the term *formulation,* as I have indicated previously, to a summary of personality functioning. In a sense a student must "formulate" his observations of intelligence test data, but this is not the sense in which the term is ordinarily used in psychiatry and psychology. Reports not employing a formulation, as the term is used here, include intelligence test reporting, reports on neurological examination, and other short, highly discreet reports covering only one aspect of a patient's functioning. Suggested outlines for these reports appear in Chapter 3.

The outlines given here may or may not be used in their present form in a final written report. How they are used in a final report is the decision of the writer. He may decide, for example, that the concepts are good in an outline but that he would not use them as headings in a written report. He may decide that he should be able to answer all the questions asked of one of the outlines but that he would not choose in every instance to write this much in a report.

Unfortunately, a formulation can be overlooked in the myriad of details required in some psychiatric case summaries. Similarly, it can be overlooked by psychologists when they use outlines which split a person into unrelated parts. The following discussion may aid you in tying a case together and may show how it is possible to avoid splitting the person. More important, it may show the range of questions the student can ask of data when he begins a report.

OUTLINE OR NO OUTLINE? From what has already been said in this manual, it is obvious that I favor using an outline for formulating a case. I find that without an outline I feel at loose ends in making interpretive notes from the data, that I forget some areas which should be discussed, and that I personally do not like a written report without at least a few headings.

In discussing writers, Barzun and Graff (1957) state:

> Writers divide fairly evenly into those who find outlines useful or indispensable, and those to whom they are a nuisance. By all means use them if they do not cost you too much in time and spontaneity. But do not force yourself to make them up if this does not come easily, or if once drawn up the outline drags you back. Certainly the best order . . . is the order that comes out of one's sense of the subject and seems dictated by it. To a writer who develops that sense from the mere growth of the data under his hand, the outline is bound to seem stiff and suspiciously logical. . . . For such a writer the better procedure is to use the outline not as a guide beforehand but as a verifier afterward [p. 238].

These statements characterize kinds of report writers and even the stages in the development of one writer. Some students feel more secure with an outline; other students feel restricted working with an outline. Writers may shift from using an outline to using none and back again to using one. Some writers use an outline for some purposes and feel no need for one in other instances.

For the best possible training, I urge you to try different outlines. Each new outline presents new questions to ask from the data. If you become flexible enough to look at data from many points of view, you may develop an outline of your own which fits you much better than an outline devised by someone else. In those rare instances in which you see "the order that comes out of one's sense of the subject and seems dictated by it," then there is, of course, no reason for you to use an outline. In general, however, your own outline is one of your greatest aids in writing reports.

THE THREE FORMS OF ORGANIZATION. There are two fundamental approaches to organizing or formulating a report about a human being: the chronological and the topical. A third approach combines the two. Barzun and Graff (1957) have beautifully contrasted the two primary approaches:

The two fundamental forms of organization may be contrasted by imagining a biography built on the one and then on the other plan:

CHRONOLOGICAL ORDER

X is born, goes to school, breaks his leg, learns to smoke, is expelled from college, studies law, meets Jane Smith, finds a five-dollar bill, is called a liar, eats lunch, gets into towering rage, marries Susan Black, is elected mayor, goes fishing, was thought a radical, plays the stock market, suffers from asthma, sues opponent for slander, reads in bed, loses Senatorial race, employs bodyguard, is accused of treason, goes to Mayo Clinic, dies. Will probated, widow marries, memoirs published.

The fault of the strict chronological order is that it mixes events great and small without due subordination, and that it combines into a parody of life incidents that occur only once with permanent truths about habits and tastes, character and belief. The mind asks for something better than this jumble; it says: "One thing at a time," meaning that it wants one subject, one idea gone into thoroughly, even if the parts of it were separated by many years. Yet the purely topical treatment will not do either:

TOPICAL ORDER

1. Character: in boyhood, youth, maturity, old age
2. Hobbies: in boyhood, youth, maturity, old age
3. Health: in boyhood, youth, maturity, old age
4. Income: in boyhood, youth, maturity, old age
5. Friends: in boyhood, youth, maturity, old age

Such a run up and down the poor man's lifespan is intolerable to contemplate, and while entailing an enormous repetition it would not leave a clear image of his life [pp. 233–234].

All personality reports in psychology and psychiatry, of course, have topics, whether the topics are made obvious by underlining or not. This is to say, the reporter in formulating the case uses certain concepts to order his data. Report writers also must handle the time factor in one way or another. Certain events come before other events, and reporters must explain why behaviors change as a result of past experiences. Furthermore, reports with a clear chronological sequence are more unified and well organized than those with no ordering of the time factor, as Barzun and Graff illustrate in their topical outline above.

The discussion which follows covers the use of all three approaches—the chronological, the topical, and the combined chronological-topical.

THE CHRONOLOGICAL APPROACH. A purely chronological report is rare in psychology and psychiatry because it requires a clarity of formulating and writing beyond the capacities (or perhaps the data) of most writers. The writer would begin at the birth of the patient (or even with statements about the parents or grandparents), then trace the development of the patient to the present, and finally make predictions about the future of the patient. This sequence would be the usual one of past, present, and future.

Such a report would be very much like a novel or biography. The writer would have to know exactly what came before what in the patient's life. As I have stated above, this is beyond the capacities of most writers and may require more data than most psychiatrists and psychologists have about a patient.

THE TOPICAL APPROACH. Topical outlines are the most frequently employed outlines in both psychology and psychiatry. They may be detailed or brief, dynamic or informational, but regardless of their form they provide a structure and are relatively easy to use. In skilled hands, topical outlines can provide the basis for informative reports without "enormous repetition." The writer who sees unity can use them without losing the unity. In the hands of a writer who does not see unity, they invite splitting the person into parts and may even prevent the writer from seeing the unity. Ordinarily topical outlines do not have a chronological dimension; this is one of their drawbacks.

The most primitive of topical outlines is the outline in which the *tests themselves* are the topics. An example of such an outline is the following:

Results of intelligence test
Results of Rorschach
Results of TAT
Results of Figure Drawings

This kind of outline obviously forces the writer to be test oriented rather than patient oriented. Few if any clinics would require such an outline, although supervisors occasionally ask for this form in order to see what their students have obtained from each test. Even for this purpose, a simple review of each test with the student would suffice to "test" the student's knowledge. The purpose of a written report is not to test the writer. The report is meant to communicate ideas about a person. The reader may be informed of what tests were used in a simple listing of tests at the beginning of a report. The reader is not appropriately concerned with the test from which an interpretation was made by the writer. The system of reporting test by test hardly fosters a formulation of the case because the emphasis is on the tests rather than on the person.

The more conventional topical outlines employ *concepts currently in use in the professional discipline of the report writer.* Psychiatrists and psychologists generally find such outlines very useful in formulating a case. This kind of outline gives an order to the thinking of the writer. But even more important, the concepts imply questions to be asked of the data. As stated previously in this manual, the difficulty students have with reports is that they do not know what questions to ask, although they may have sufficient knowledge to give answers.

While later I shall show my own preference for an outline which introduces a chronological dimension to formulating cases, I believe that the purely topical outline may aid students in seeing the kinds of questions they might ask of the data. Even writers who have developed their own outlines may find in the following examples some areas of interest which have never occurred to them before.

For organizing psychological reports, W. Klopfer (1960) suggests the following outline:

Behavior during testing
Intellectual aspects of the personality

Affective aspects of the personality
Basic conflict areas
Adaptive and maladaptive techniques
Diagnostic indicators
Prognostic implications [p. 36]

This is typical of the outlines used in organizing the results of psychological testing. It covers some of the major conceptualizations currently used in psychology and psychiatry. The topics are discrete; but to the extent that the user sees them as discrete, the outline will invite splitting the person into parts.

Another topical method of formulation is in terms of *strengths* and *weaknesses*. Similar to this is a formulation revolving around *successes* and *failures*. These forms are generally used for presentation to a supervisor, but could be used to write the body of a report. The simplicity in both is admirable, but a great deal of sophistication is required to use such a simple conceptualization of a person.

Clinicians who are strongly dedicated to a particular *school* or *theory* sometimes use a form which covers all of the constructs of the theory. The dangers here are that the patient may be fitted to the theory and that the reader may not think in terms of the constructs. The obvious ways to avoid these dangers are (1) to use a theory as a framework, (2) not to be tied to using all the constructs, and (3) to use behavioral rather than theoretical terms in the final report.

Bellak (1954) suggests the following outline for reporting on the Thematic Apperception Test. While this form would not ordinarily be used for a test battery or psychiatric interview report, it is quoted here because it may alert report writers to a simple and unified structure for analyzing data. It stresses thinking in terms of (1) how the patient perceives himself (hero) and (2) the central themes of his life.

1. The main theme 2. The main hero 3. Main needs of the hero	Unconscious structure and needs of the subject
4. The conception of the environment 5. Figures seen as . . .	His conception of the world and of significant figures around him
6. Significant conflicts 7. Nature of anxieties 8. Main defenses 9. Severity of superego 10. The integration of the ego	Dimensions of personality

[pp. 51–57]

Summarizing differently from the way Bellak suggests in the right-hand column, one may conceptualize the patient in terms of:

1. Needs
2. Perception of the environment
3. Conflicts
4. Resulting anxieties
5. Defenses against anxiety
6. Integrating factors

This outline could provide an excellent progression of ideas. There is in my rephrasing of Bellak's outline a sequential order. The order, however, relates to the patient's functioning at this moment. It revolves around the present; it does not invite a discussion of the past or future of the patient. Thus it is orderly but not chronological in the sense of discussing past and future. If the report writer needs only a discussion of present functioning, either Bellak's outline or my restatement of the outline may serve the purpose very well.

Somewhat similar is the following outline which I have designed to illustrate a comprehensive topical format for formulating a case. The psychiatrist may or may not feel he has enough data to discuss the first section; it is ordinarily employed by psychologists if they have given intelligence tests.

1. *Intellectual functioning*
   Level of present functioning
   Level of capacity
   Reasons for failure to function up to capacity
   Areas of strengths and weaknesses
2. *Conflicts*
   Major and minor conflicts
   People with whom conflicts are manifested
   Times and places where conflicts arise
   Etiology of conflicts
3. *Methods of handling conflicts*
   Manifestations of anxiety, symptoms, defense mechanisms
   Overt behavior
4. *Strengths and weaknesses in relation to goals*
   Needs and wishes, manifest and latent
   Strengths for pursuing them
   Weaknesses
5. *Recommendations*
   Therapy or no therapy, environmental change
   Form of therapy
   Predictions about therapy

There is an order to this outline but it is not a simple chronological order. The past of the patient can be discussed in three different places (reasons for failure to function up to capacity, etiology of conflicts, and weaknesses). This outline in particular illustrates how a format can be topically comprehensive but not have a simple and unified chronological sequence.

If we eliminate simple chronology, as the above outlines do, we run the risk of failing to see what produces what. Instead we choose an area of functioning, explain it as well as we can, and then shift to another area. This allows us, indeed invites us, to mix the chronology and to split a person into parts.

A way to avoid this splitting is to combine the topical approach with a simple chronology.

THE CHRONOLOGICAL-TOPICAL APPROACH. A format combining the topical and chronological approaches is suggested by Karl Menninger (1952); he calls it a "diagnostic synthesis."

I. The personality development and structure
  A. Heredo-congenital nucleus of the personality
  B. The general conditioning of childhood
  C. Special conditioning of childhood
  D. Data of the adolescent period relevant to present illness
  E. Maturity
II. The environment (present)
III. The maladjustment (precipitating causes, anxiety, insight, facade, defenses, focus of aggression discharge, secondary gains, approach to treatment) [pp. 101–105. See these pages for details.]

The sequence of this outline is past, present, and future, although the future is only dimly referred to. The outline might be restated more simply:

Heredo-congenital factors
Development of personality
Present environment
Reaction to the environment
Approach to treatment

Menninger adds a diagnostic summary to the above outline. It is quoted here because of the additional factors it suggests for observation.

IV. Diagnostic summary
    A. Personality type
    B. Psychiatric syndrome
    C. Medical, surgical, and dental complications
    D. Unclassified symptomatic manifestations not included above
    E. Sociological status, including economic situation
    F. It is required in many places to add to the name-diagnosis of psychiatric illnesses the following:
        1. Brief description of syndrome, severity, and duration
        2. The precipitating stress
        3. Degree of predisposition recognized in the premorbid personality
        4. Degree of incapacity [pp. 105–106]

The following is an outline suggested by Noyes and Kolb (1958) for formulation after psychiatric interview and examination:

1. Summary of patient's problems
    a. Behavioral disturbances
    b. Psychological disturbances
    c. Emotional disturbances
    d. Physiological (somatic) disturbances
2. Salient features of genetic, constitutional, familial and environmental influences
3. Psychodynamic explanation
4. Diagnostic classification
5. Therapeutic formulation
6. Prognostic evaluation [pp. 160–161. See these pages for details.]

The emphasis in this outline is primarily centered on disturbance or pathology. Its sequence is present, past, and future.

I favor my own chronological-topical outline because of its request for discussion of strengths and its behavioral orientation.

1. *Functioning*
   How does the patient presently behave overtly with others? Alone?
   Relation between intellectual functioning, capacity, and other factors
2. *Dynamics*
   What is he attempting to accomplish with his present mode of behavior?
   What thoughts and feelings is he having?
   What events or people produce conflict, anxiety?
   What are the conflicts?
3. *Development*
   How did his present situation arise?
   What pressures and supports were given by significant figures?
   What was the sequence of learning his defenses, symptoms, adaptations, etc.?
4. *Prognosis*
   What are the pressures, supports, and strengths (environmental and intrapsychic) which can change his life?
   What can produce dangerous and/or crippling behavior (suicide, psychotic reactions, psychosomatic difficulties, antisocial acts)?
   What does he need in order to function more effectively?
   How much impairment is there? What is the nature of the impairment?
   Is psychotherapy necessary or desirable? By whom?
   What other forms of therapy?

The sequence of this outline is present, past, and future. This sequence has the advantage of first presenting the patient as one sees him today, then explaining his development, and finally giving his predicted future. This allows us to begin where the patient is at this moment, with his presenting problem and behavior in the clinic or hospital. An example of a report written with this kind of outline is given in Example H in the last chapter.

As stated previously, any outline can potentially provide the basis for brilliant reports on people. If the case is well formulated, the writer sees all the data as unified and related. The question is, why make the task difficult? To make the job as easy as possible, a combined topical and chronological format is probably most helpful.

Some examples of various kinds of reports will be found at the end of this manual. A study of them will reveal that clinicians use many different formats and produce excellent reports. I urge the student to try all of the outlines given here in order to find what suits his own personality and style. I can think of no better experience for learning to write reports.

III. OUTLINES FOR REPORTS IN SPECIAL AREAS

Psychologists and psychiatrists are called upon to write reports for many purposes and many kinds of institutions. The best formats for most purposes are simple, exclude what is not pertinent, include everything that is pertinent, have few sections, and allow the reader to find quickly what he wants on rereading the report.

The formulation discussed previously is the foundation of reports for most purposes. The outlines and comments which follow may be helpful to the reader in preparing the final written reports, either of total personality functioning or of a more discrete nature.

A GENERAL OUTLINE FOR PSYCHOLOGICAL REPORTS. Psychological test reporting can take many forms. Most clinics and hospitals have a general format.

The following general outline is given for those who do not have a specific form to follow:

REPORT OF PSYCHOLOGICAL EXAMINATION

CONFIDENTIAL—FOR PROFESSIONAL USE ONLY

Name of Patient: Date of Examination:

Date of Birth: Tests Administered:

Referred by:

Referral Statement:

(A brief statement of why the patient was referred for testing.)

Test Behavior:

(Usually brief descriptions of appearance or test behavior which are pertinent to purposes of the report.)

Test Results:

(The *formulation of the case* resulting from the analysis of test results.)

Summary and Recommendations:

(Summary should be brief. Recommendations should be as detailed as is appropriate to the clinic for which it is written.)

REPORTING ON INTELLIGENCE. Any reporting on intelligence, whether it is one paragraph or a detailed report, can be static or very meaningful and dynamic. To give as much meaning as possible to intellectual functioning, the student should consider the following issues:

1. Level of functioning; estimate of level of "capacity" (i.e., in what areas could he be expected to function more effec-

tively if circumstances, or his "adjustment," were different?)
2. Functioning in various intellectual areas
3. Relationship between intelligence and the patient's total functioning
4. Relationship between patient's intelligence and that of his group

Many reports give only the *level* of intelligence. Sometimes this is all that is asked for. Since level of intelligence is given so much attention, this should be stated simply in a short paragraph standing alone. For example, in a clinic report where the concept IQ is employed, the following statement is appropriate:

> On the WISC, this child obtained a verbal IQ of 93, a performance IQ of 95, resulting in a full-scale IQ of 94. This places him in the average range of intelligence.

In personnel reports the following statement may be used:

> Mr. A has very superior intelligence. This places him in the upper two percent of the general population and above the average of executive personnel.

Whatever figures you use should be absolutely clear to your reader. If, for example, T scores are used, you should explain their meaning.

The reporting of intelligence is a constant problem to psychologists. This is because the concept of intelligence is so widely misunderstood. Possible misuse of intelligence ratings has been widely cited as one of the most prevalent risks in the practice of psychology and psychiatry. Because of the great dependence on intelligence ratings in our culture at the present time, both professionals and students should carefully study the meaning of intelligence before they use the concept in their practice.

Many psychologists, in their attempt to give a complete account of intellectual functioning, produce an analysis of functioning in various areas. This is often obtained from a "pattern analysis" of intelligence test scores, although also from responses to the Rorschach and other tests. The psychology student should be aware of the complications and objections to such a procedure. (See Cohen, 1957a; Cohen, 1957b; Cohen, 1959; Derner, Aborn, & Canter, 1950.) That is, if he does a pattern analysis, he should be aware of its limitations and its inherent error.

Some reports of intelligence are replete with references to "rote memory," "fund of information from the environment," and the like. In making such statements, the student should keep two considerations in mind. The most important is that in translating a test score into a statement about a patient, we may have little or no scientific evidence that the score means what we say. (See Cohen, 1957a; Cohen, 1957b; Cohen, 1959.) The student should be thoroughly familiar with the literature on interpretation of intelligence test scores, and then if he chooses state his opinion in the report. A report is a statement of opinions, but they should be opinions based on study. Second, interpretations of test scores should provide meaningful information to the reader, i.e., information relevant to his interests. The frequent reference to "rote memory" in psychological reports, for example, is completely useless to the reader in many instances.

You may also choose to relate intellectual functioning to the person's *total functioning*. Once you have developed the experience and sophistication to discuss intellectual "areas," you should then attempt to relate your interpretations to meaningful aspects of the client's life. You might attempt a prediction of the patient's performance with various kinds of problems and in varying situations. These elements and his general level may even be related to the particular therapeutic demands which may be placed on the patient. For example, low intelligence or poor verbal abstract ability may in your opinion have a strong influence on the efficacy of psychotherapy.

The fourth item listed above relates to the relationship between the patient's intelligence and that of his *group*, i.e., the kinds of people he has to live with. Psychologists seldom discuss comparisons of this nature, although discrepancies may have a marked influence on the patient's adjustment. A notation of this kind can bring a report to life. For example, an adolescent's average IQ may be noted but not related to any other factors in his life; relating this fact to his necessity for constant relationship with a prep school group of very superior intelligence may be crucial to his adjustment problems. Similar examples are the husband of average intelligence married to a very superior wife, a man of superior intelligence working as a janitor, an executive of average intelligence in competition with peers of very superior intelligence.

For a lengthier discussion of intelligence as related to clinical work, see Derner and Aborn (1949).

PSYCHOLOGISTS' REPORTS FOR NEUROLOGISTS. Psychologists are frequently called upon to assist neurologists in differential diagnosis. In this role the psychologist is sometimes not clear on what specifically he is being asked for and how complete his report should be.

> It has been found that the neurologist and neurosurgeon chiefly want information about intellectual and memory functioning, together with distortions in personality which are very useful for diagnosis of structural pathology or for differential diagnosis between organic and functional conditions (i.e., symptomatic epilepsy; hysterical components relative to the absence of organic findings in low back pain, etc.) [Morrow, 1954, p. 108].

Morrow (1954) suggests the following outline for reporting to neurologists:

1. IQ
2. Estimated comparison with premorbid functioning
3. Memory function and areas of difficulty
4. Concrete vs. abstract thinking
5. Aphasia and other language problems
6. Personality functioning only as relevant to these [p. 108]

This is an appropriate outline for *most* psychological reports to neurologists. I have pointed out elsewhere in this manual that the safest way to know how much you should include in any kind of report is to talk to the reader.

INDUSTRIAL (VOCATIONAL) REPORTS. Industrial psychologists, psychiatrists, and clinical psychologists working in industry or writing other kinds of vocationally oriented reports are faced with a number of problems not found in clinics. (1) They must communicate in language which can be understood by the layman. (2) They ordinarily write about the present and the future, excluding the past or developmental history. (3) They must write under categories of special interest to business organizations.

These special requirements make writing for industry a unique experience, one which might be helpful to all clinicians and one which provides training in preparing reports that can be obtained in almost no other way—training in writing clear and simple English, training in making unequivocal professional judgments and predicting behavior (which surprisingly we can do very well), and training in thinking along "unpsychological" but very important practical lines. This last point may be illustrated by looking at the categories used in reports of this kind.

Fear (1958), in a book on the evaluation interview in industry, suggests the following outline as a guide for interviewing and report writing.

1. Test results
   Mental ability, numerical ability, verbal ability, clerical aptitude (or some other test results, depending upon the needs of the case), social intelligence.
2. Evaluation
   Work history; education and training; early home background; present social adjustment; personality, motivation and character.
3. Summary of assets and liabilities.
4. Summary. [from Examples, pp. 260–278]

The psychological consulting firm of Rohrer, Hibler, and Replogle uses only five general categories. Their reports are usually no longer than one and a half pages, single spaced; they do not employ headings. Their outline is as follows:

1. Intelligence
2. Emotional control
3. Skill in human relations
4. Insight and self-criticism
5. Organization and planning ability; direction of others

Recommendation and prognosis (for candidates)
Conclusions and prognosis (for non-candidates)

The consulting firm of Richardson, Bellows, Henry and Co. writes a longer report and titles each "area" for the reader. Their outline is as follows:

1. Intellectual functioning
2. Relations with others
3. Work characteristics
4. Aspirations and drive
5. Interests and values
6. Personal adjustment
7. Family background
8. Potential and recommendations

A report written by the author using the format of Richardson, Bellows, Henry and Co. is given in Example G in Chapter VIII, "Some Examples of Report Writing."

Writing for industry or other vocational situations is in one important respect a somewhat easier task than writing clinical reports. We have, if we take advantage of it, some criteria against which to judge the person about whom the report is written. These criteria come from the reader. Much of the report centers on the person's qualifications for a particular position, and the reader can give us the criteria if we know how to get them from him. Without these criteria our reports are apt to be vacuous, overly technical, or unhelpful.

Asking your reader one or more of the following questions may be helpful to you in writing your report:

What characteristics are you looking for in a man for this job?

What characteristics of this man, as you see him, stand in the way of your hiring him without any hesitation?

What specific questions keep coming into your mind about the candidate?

Describe the characteristics of the most satisfactory man you can think of in this job. (This might be an actual or imaginary "ideal" employee, depending on whether the job has existed before.)

What do you *not* want in a man for this job?

The ideal way to obtain your criteria is to interview or test a group of top employees and a group of poor employees working in this position. This is a time-consuming and expensive method but without any question the most productive. Even when this is possible, the questions listed above should be asked of the people who know the position well.

For this kind of reporting, you are really writing blindly if you have no criteria. Because criteria are available in this situation, psychologists and psychiatrists have a great deal to offer the area of vocational planning. We are certainly not in such a fortunate position in our clinical work, where the criteria for judgment (of health, illness, prognosis, etc.) invite so many disagreements.

PSYCHIATRIC CASE SUMMARIES. Psychiatric case summaries usually include records of physical examination, mental and physical history, and psychological examination.

The writer should clarify the purpose of case summaries. In general the report is written for one or both of two purposes —to aid in the care of the patient or for record keeping. In either case the aim of the report is to aid some future reader in understanding the patient; this should be the primary consideration of the writer.

The two case summaries which follow are among the most complete used in psychiatry. The psychiatric resident may find them helpful if he has not been given a form to follow. The psychologist may find in them suggestions for making his own reports more complete.

Wolberg's outline for a case summary (1954, pp. 684–685) is as follows:

a. Chief complaint (in patient's own words)
b. History and development of complaint (date of onset, circumstances under which complaint developed, progression from the onset to the time of the initial interview)
c. Other complaints and symptoms (physical, emotional, psychic and behavior symptoms other than those of the complaint factor)
d. Medical, surgical, and in women, gynecologic history
e. Environmental disturbance at onset of therapy (economic, work, housing, neighborhood and family difficulties)
f. Relationship difficulties at onset of therapy (disturbances in relationships with people, attitudes toward the world, toward authority and toward the self)

g. Hereditary, constitutional and early developmental influences (significant physical and psychiatric disorders in patient's family, socio-economic status of family, important early traumatic experiences and relationships, neurotic traits in childhood and adolescence)
h. Family data (mother, father, siblings, spouse, children—ages, state of health, personality adjustment, and patient's attitude toward each)
i. Previous attacks of emotional illness (as a child and later). When did patient feel himself to be completely free from emotional illness?
j. Initial interview (brief description of condition of patient at initial interview, including clinical findings)
k. Level of insight and motivation at onset of therapy (How long did the patient feel that he needed treatment? For what? Awareness of emotional nature of problem. Willingness to accept psychotherapy.)
l. Previous treatments (When did the patient first seek treatment? What treatment did he get? Any hospitalization?)
m. Clinical examination (significant findings in physical, neurological, psychiatric and psychologic examinations)
n. Differential diagnosis (at time of initial interview)
o. Estimate of prognosis (at time of initial interview)
p. Psychodynamics and psychopathology
q. Course of treatment:
   (1) Type of therapy employed, frequency, total number of sessions, response to therapist
   (2) Significant events during therapy, dynamics that were revealed, verbatim report of important dreams, nature of transference and resistance
   (3) Progress in therapy, insight acquired, translation of insight into action, change in symptoms, attitudes and relationships with people
r. Condition on discharge (areas of improvement, remaining problems)
s. Recommendations to patient
t. Statistical classification

This outline is extremely comprehensive. Its function is primarily to record everything known about the patient. One would be hard pressed to find anything that is left out; I quote it here to serve as a basic format which you may want to vary for your own purposes. Certainly for comprehensive clinic or hospital records, it could hardly be improved.

Menninger's outline (1952, pp. 138–140) which follows requests more summarizing than does Wolberg's. It also requires that the writer state specifically the function of the summary, and everything that follows this statement is, by implication, written to serve this function. Thus, you may prefer this outline when you are preparing a summary for a function other than the usual clinic or hospital record.

1. *Identification of the patient and problem:*
   a. File number, age, sex, color, marital status, occupation and residence. . . .
   b. Referring physician or agency.
   c. Date of admission (unless included above).
   d. Presenting complaints or reason for original referral.
   e. Location of patient at time of the summary.
   f. Function of his summary. State whether it has been prepared for the use of the nurses, for a consultant, for a staff presentation, for an adjudication board, or for a referring physician or agency.
   g. If there is a special problem to be solved at a conference for which this summary is prepared, e.g., the question of discharge from hospital, state what the problem is.
2. *Background:* Summarize those facets in the family history, infancy, childhood, school, social, occupational, sexual and military history that are pertinent to the diagnosis or the reason for presentation.
3. *Present illness:* Condense into a terse outline the major events and developments, including the more important symptoms leading up to examination or hospitalization. . . .
4. *Examination data:* A separate paragraph should be written under each of these sub-headings.

a. Physical and neurological examination: (Pathology found.)
b. Laboratory and X-ray examination: (Significant findings only.)
c. Psychological examination: Here you may copy the summary made of the Psychological Examination. This is the most important paragraph in most psychiatric case study summaries. Both assets and pathology should be included. . . .

5. *Course of illness in hospital, or while under observation elsewhere:* Include treatment given and response thereto, complications that have developed, and speed and trend of movement in the case. . . . Include recent opinions of (other) consultants. . . . This should lead up to a formulation of:
6. *Present status* of the patient on (always give date) with reference to:
   a. his illness; (recovered, improved, unchanged.)
   b. his treatment program; (continued hospitalization with what general regime; gone home; ready for discharge; waiting to begin psychoanalysis; etc.)
   c. (for VA patients) service connected disabilities, if any; (unchanged, improved, or not examined.)
7. *Diagnoses:*
   a. Personality type. . . .
   b. Psychiatric syndrome. . . .
   c. Medical, surgical, and dental complications. . . .
   d. Unclassified symptomatic manifestation not included above.
   e. Sociological status, including economic situation. . . .
8. *Subsequent treatment contemplated or recommended.* . . .
9. *Prognosis:* This may have been implied in the foregoing. If not, a statement may be attempted here if desired.

SPECIAL SITUATIONS. Almost all varieties of reports discussed in this chapter might be written by the private practitioner. Professionals in private practice are also requested to produce reports for courts, psychoanalytic clinics, referring physicians, and other individuals and institutions.

Naturally, if the reporter can speak with the reader, he will ask what kind of report is expected of him, what needs to be answered about the patient. In private practice, however, many writers are given only the briefest of request forms, and speaking to the reader is not possible. If you do not know exactly what is expected of you, the following questions may serve as a guide, since they are usually what is being asked:

What is the matter with the patient? This implies, What is wrong? Despite the fact that the referring agent asks only this question, it is not only appropriate but necessary to answer, What is "right" with the patient?

What should be done? Remember that the referring person has a responsibility and wants to discharge it with dispatch. He is asking your help in doing this.

The caution you must exercise in answering these questions is the subject of a large part of this manual. For example, to answer what is "wrong" with the patient you cannot wisely answer with a diagnosis of schizophrenic reaction unless you are certain that the reader knows your implications.

The difficulty in writing reports for unknown readers is that so many of your statements are "shots in the dark" as to communicating anything, and even more serious is the fact that you do not know what effect your statements may have on the future of a person. One word (e.g., "schizophrenic") may hamper a person's chance of being accepted as a patient for treatment in a low-cost psychotherapeutic service, remove or delay a court sentence, or produce any number of extremely serious effects on a person's career.

There are few helpful rules to cover these risks. Again, the best rule is to make every effort to talk to your reader. Other "rules" will be discussed in the chapter on confidentiality.

IV. THERAPY PROGRESS NOTES

Writing notes on what occurs in a therapeutic session is not ordinarily thought of as report writing. Progress recording is, however, a major form of reporting required of so many psychiatrists and psychologists that a discussion of some of its problems is highly appropriate in a manual of this kind.

When students and friends discuss their cases with me we sometimes discover startling things—that the therapist is frightened of the patient, that he dislikes the patient, that he should have transferred the patient to another therapist long ago, that he has completely identified with the patient, that he should never have taken the patient in the first place. There are two ways to keep abreast of therapy progress. One is to be in constant supervision. Most of us, however, are not fortunate enough, for numerous reasons, to have supervision available. The other way to be aware of therapy progress is to take careful records.

Students ask many questions about progress recording. What function do the notes serve? Should notes be taken during or after therapy sessions? How much needs to be recorded? How can I avoid distortions when attempting to summarize a session? Do I endanger the patient's future by recording certain intimate material in the files of a clinic or hospital?

Some clinicians do not have the freedom to write notes as they would choose, because the form is set for them by the institution in which they practice. Social workers, for example, often have a very fixed method of progress recording. Psychiatrists and psychologists, on the other hand, are seldom trained to take good progress notes. The following comments are addressed to those who are not required to follow a set pattern and to those who are dissatisfied with their present methods.

NOTES OR NO NOTES? Writing meaningful and helpful notes on a fifty-minute therapy session is not an easy job. Some therapists avoid the complications by simply not taking any notes. Menninger's (1952) position is this:

> Every ship has its log, and the progress of every patient who has been carefully studied and launched on a program of treatment . . . should be just as carefully charted. As treatment proceeds, changes take place both in the patient and in the physician. In a sense, one has to chart simultaneously the progress of the illness (its resolution or further extension), the progress of the patient in getting well, and the progress of the physician in understanding the patient and the disease process.
>
> All this would seem to be most obvious and most important, but sad to relate, it is one of the weakest features in most psychiatric records. The so-called progress notes made by the psychiatrist tend to be either unsystematic, irregular, too replete with details or else trite, meaningless and repetitious [p. 127].

A few clinicians claim that recording of any kind distorts the therapeutic relationship; they say that what transpires in a session should take whatever form it takes in the mind of the therapist. To take notes, they insist, is to label, to fix, to prevent the fluid and dynamic quality of the relationship.

My own point of view is that therapy notes serve an extremely important function. Primarily they are for the patient's welfare. For the therapist, notes provide an opportunity to review what has been transpiring and allow him the constant opportunity to reformulate the case and its progress. It may even be that one of the reasons most therapy continues for such an extended period is that some therapists do not continually attempt to formulate what is going on, how the patient is faring, and what the therapist's feelings are. If therapists took the job of writing notes seriously, they might find they are not helping some patients and should shift them to other therapists. Therapists might also find that study of carefully written progress notes may even aid in cutting down the treatment period.

HOW AND WHEN TO TAKE NOTES. In our training programs we assume that students know how to take notes. Often, however, neither the mechanics nor the rationale of note taking has been taught to students.

The simplest, most accurate, and most time-saving methods are to take notes during the interview or mechanically record the interview. Students, however, often find these methods anxiety-provoking for themselves and, they think, inhibiting to patients. The easiest way to solve the latter problem is to ask the patient how he feels about either method. If the patient consents to one method or the other and later changes his mind, the method can be changed. Most patients do not find either method disturbing.

On occasion the therapist will feel that, at special times in a session, note taking is not advisable. This may be because of the extremely personal nature of what is being said (e.g., a tearful and deeply felt account of a tragic incident) or because the patient is in a highly emotional or perhaps paranoid state. In some circumstances taking notes is about as sensitive a thing to do as taking notes during a funeral.

Some therapists completely reject the idea of taking notes in the presence of the patient. Sullivan's (1954) views are:

. . . if enough attention is paid to them so they are legible, this is very apt indeed to interfere with things of much greater importance to the patient, if not to the [therapist].

The . . . interviewer is supposed to be doing three things: considering what the patient could mean by what he says; considering how he himself can best phrase what he wished to communicate to the patient; and, at the same time, observing the general pattern of the events being communicated or discussed. In addition to that, to make notes which will be of more than evocative value, or come anywhere near being a verbatim record of what is said, in my opinion is beyond the capacity of most human beings [p. 50].

My own view is that the amount of interference note taking brings to the therapist is an individual matter. The only way you can answer the question for yourself is to try different methods.

If you want a complete verbatim record of therapeutic sessions, the only way to procure it is to record the interviews mechanically. Therapists find that this does not interfere with therapy. The fact is that once the machine is on, both patient and therapist are apt to forget it. For supervision the tape is very effective, but of course very time consuming. Every therapist should tape sessions periodically. To hear the sound of your own voice and particularly to hear what you and the patient *actually said* can give you some extremely valuable insights into all phases of your therapeutic practice.

A new method of studying the therapeutic process is the use of motion pictures. At present the great cost of this procedure makes it available only to researchers with fairly large financial grants. With further mechanical progress, this method may in the future be available to the individual practitioner.

The whole matter of recording therapy sessions in the presence of the patient may be put this way: use any method that is comfortable for both yourself and the patient, does not interfere with your relationship, and meets your time and expense restrictions. Students should, however, try different methods before rejecting them on the basis of what they *think* they would not like.

Some therapists take notes during the interview or record sessions, file them away for "reference," and never use them. The point of this manual is that reports are written to be read. Therapy notes or tapes are useful only if studied by the therapist. Regardless of the kind of record kept, you should attempt a formulation of what has transpired during therapy. While it is unrealistic to believe that you will have the time to do this after each session, you should at least attempt such formulation frequently and at regular intervals in the course of therapy.

If recording the interview in the presence of the patient is rejected, you are left with note taking after the interview. This should by all means be done immediately. Few therapists can later recall accurately what was said in a session, especially if one or more therapeutic hours intervene. You may even have to cut a session short in order to take satisfactory notes; it is worth it if you want an accurate record.

One further word for beginning therapists: if the patient is confusing you, take a verbatim record. You may find that your impression of the patient in face-to-face contact is totally different from the impression you get from reading or hearing a tape of what he has said. A startling thing to discover is that what seemed during a session to be "natural" and "normal" although somewhat confusing turns out to be clear psychotic production when the verbatim record is reviewed.

WHAT IS INCLUDED. As Menninger (1952, p. 127) says, progress notes "tend to be either unsystematic, irregular, too replete with details or else trite, meaningless and repetitious." Progress notes are often poor because (1) most clinicians have developed no system to follow, and (2) most clinicians are undecided on the question of whom the notes are written for. One must answer as well as he can the question, To whom am I writing? There are some facts available to answer this question. These "facts" include your own practice needs, the possible transfer of the patient to another hospital or therapist, and the necessity to discuss the case with a supervisor or in staff conference. You should make the best decision you can and then continually keep in mind the use to which the notes will be put.

As to what is actually written down, the recorder should consider what kind of data might be meaningful to the reader. Two annoying kinds of progress notes to read are those consisting only of psychodynamic interpretations and those consisting strictly of what transpired in the interview. The first gives *only* what the reporter thought; the second gives *nothing* of what the reporter thought.

The following is an interpretive account:

Progress—No oral references. Transference increasing. Annoyed at gray screen. Oedipal material showing up.

These notes are perhaps appropriate for the therapist himself but would be mystifying to another reader.

The following is a behavioral account:

Patient arrived 32 minutes late. Talked about mother and her desire to be a singer. Shifted to his own musical talents and where he hopes to go in music. "I'd like to be as good as Lotte Lehman." Spoke of music school and how he hates it. More about expense of school, etc., and "Aren't your fees higher than most clinics?" At end of session asked how much longer he would have to come. Angry that I would not make up his lost 32 minutes.

These notes list briefly what occurred in the session but give no interpretations. This session may have been an important one to the therapist. The notes have hints of information about structure, dynamics, and developmental history and also hints of the nature of the relationship between patient and therapist. This may be enough for the therapist himself, but even he may have difficulty later in recalling his interpretation of the content. From these notes the reader (for example, a subsequent therapist) can be sure of nothing except content. Missing are the answers to numerous questions: What did the patient's arriving late mean? Why the quote about Lotte Lehman? What significance does the statement about termination have?

If you attempt to include both content and interpretation, there are some lists of relevant data which you may use as guideposts.

Wolberg (1954) states that if one wished to go beyond a single sentence giving the dominant theme of an interview, the following other entries may be made:

a. Present state of symptoms or complaints (absent, improved, the same, worse)
b. How the patient feels (anxious, placid, depressed, happy)
c. Important life situations and developments since last visit and how they were handled
d. Content of the session
e. Significant transference and resistance reactions
f. Dreams (Since the wording of the patient's dreams is important, it is best to write dreams down during the session while they are related by the patient) [pp. 683–684].

If such a list is employed, the recorder should make clear what was observed behaviorally and what the recorder implies or *interprets* from the verbal or other behavior.

A significant omission on Wolberg's list is the noting of *countertransference*. This might be the last item.

Wolberg further suggests a monthly progress summary on

the patient's response to therapy. His form for this summary is a checklist including the following:

> General progress to date
> Appointments (late, on time, etc.)
> Communicativeness
> Relationship with therapist
> Resistance
> Insight
> Translation of insight into action
> Present symptoms
> [pp. 819–820; refer to these pages for details]

If such a checklist is employed, the reporter may wish to add *goals of therapy* as seen by the therapist.

Complete progress notes also include all significant events relating to the patient *between interviews*. Menninger (1952) lists these as follows:

1. The extent to which the patient accepts and follows the therapeutic program.
2. Steps taken by the physician and others to overcome the patient's resistance to the therapeutic program, and if this involves the patient's relatives, the steps taken by the physician and others in interpreting the treatment recommendations to them and obtaining their cooperation.
3. Changes in symptomatology, if any.
4. The dates and details of any special therapeutic procedures such as electroshock, together with the patient's immediate reaction thereto.
5. Interviews or telephone conversations relating to the patient. Social workers are much better about keeping such records than are psychiatrists, but many a complication has arisen because of a physician's failure to include a notation regarding the content of a telephone call.
6. The results of consultations with colleagues.
7. Changes in medication and in any other details of the therapeutic program.

8. Accidents, injuries, attempted elopements and other marked changes in the physical, psychological or environmental status of the patient should always be dictated immediately and fully by the psychiatrist [p. 128].

Fries and Friedman (1960) have suggested a method of organizing clinical data for teaching residents in psychoanalytic psychotherapy. Their method has the following emphases:

1. The recording of the total data on a patient to include material from the treatment sessions, behavior and attitudes in the hospital, choice of friends, selection of clothes, participation in hospital activities, circumstances at home, behavior toward family on home visits, etc.
2. The way in which, within the framework of the psychoanalytic approach, the data can be used by the resident in understanding the patient by observing changes.
3. The need consistently to include in the daily notes—the unexplained behavior, comments and trends, since these are usually important and too often lost.
4. The role of the supervisor in the handling of the case, which, unless recorded, is either incorporated or ignored, and in either event "lost."
5. Awareness and constant comment by the therapist of countertransference factors.
6. Consistent focus on the concepts of psychoanalytic psychotherapy, and specific, well-defined, limited goals.
7. The therapist's role in the treatment situation. When the therapist can be made aware of the multiple factors pertinent to the current situation, and be sensitive to the patient's needs and reactions, he can more easily choose, at any given time, where to focus treatment.
8. The material is recorded in a form available for future research [pp. 40–41].

They suggest a data sheet of vertical columns with the following headings:

Date
Life situation
Material in session
How understood by therapist
Unexplained material
What supervisor showed therapist
Approach, planned and unplanned
[pp. 42–43]

The authors also suggest a periodic phase summary which reviews the data sheets.

While the lists given here may seem voluminous, they can be followed easily. Regardless of format, the actual notes must be brief. Most therapists have a total of ten minutes between patients, and most readers do not have the time to study lengthy records.

To summarize the above, the following list covers the topics necessary in progress notes:

1. Brief notes on what transpired behaviorally—i.e., what the patient and interviewer said, how the patient acted.
2. Interpretations of the content of the interview—i.e., what the therapist thought or felt was going on in the interview, how this affects the progress of the patient.
3. Notes on countertransference (the "feelings" of the therapist).
4. Anything which occurs between sessions—telephone calls, letters written, etc.

NOTES ON COUNTERTRANSFERENCE. As previously stated in this manual, no report can be written only on the reporter's "feelings" although they do comprise crucial data for almost any kind of report.

Notes on the therapist's feelings cannot be left to chance good memory, especially when the therapist is handling numerous cases. The following are some countertransference notes which were found to be very helpful to one therapist.

Do I like this patient? His dependency seems to irritate me. Watch if it continues. Does patient know this?

I seem overly fond of this child. Identification with his problems? Or?

Had dream about patient night following this session. Pt. was walking on 55th St. I shook hands with her and. . . .

These kinds of notations serve two purposes. First, they make the therapist even more cognizant of countertransference than he normally may be. Further, they give him the data from which to formulate the meaning of his feelings.

NOTES FOR THE NEXT INTERVIEW. Notes referring to what must be done before or during subsequent interviews should be prominently placed in progress notes. The therapist does not always find the time to go over his complete notes on the previous interview. What is often essential is to know what promises he made to the patient, what he wishes to pursue in the next interview, and what questions he needs to ask.

There are simple ways to do this. Either paragraphing or underlining will stand out on quick perusal.

Pt. still depressed. I did not ask about suicidal thoughts but I suspect them. I asked if he felt that he would like to go to a hospital. He's not sure but asked me to investigate. I will call H Hospital to find out about possibilities for referral. Suspect he has been waiting for me to suggest it. . . .

V. SOME NOTES ON WHAT TO WRITE

Many psychiatrists and psychologists do everything they can to avoid writing reports if it is not a central part of their jobs. New students in both professions find the task very difficult and many dislike it. The formulation is hard enough to develop, but then we must proceed to the writing of the report and that offers its own special problems.

The difficulties of writing the report center around a number of questions which come to our mind as we write. How long should the report be? Does anyone ever read it? Is it useful? How much of what I know should I include? What should I do with uninterpretable data? How should I describe the patient's appearance and behavior in the clinic? Do I quote my data or only interpret it? How do I handle the impressions of previous examiners?

This chapter offers some answers to these questions.

HOW LONG SHOULD A REPORT BE? Common problems in report writing are: How much do you include? How much of what you know should you say? How long should the report be?

Tallent and Reiss (1959) have studied the spontaneous suggestions of psychiatrists, social workers, and psychologists for the content of *psychological* reports. Some of their conclusions are:

> The psychiatrists and social workers appear to be much more interested in having a statement of IQ or intelligence level than the psychologists are in reporting it. . . . Recommendations regarding treatment, the item of content which the psychologist wishes most to convey, is spontaneously mentioned by a relatively small number of psychiatrists . . . however, half of the social workers in the sample suggested the desirability of receiving psychological recommendations. . . .
>
> The psychiatrists, much more so than is true of psychologists and social workers, expressed interest in learning from psychological reports about the orderliness of thought processes and about the presence of organicity. . . . Relatively little general concern is shown with pathology . . . more emphasis is placed on the overall personality picture . . . nor is there an emphasis on learning of the presence of an underlying psychosis . . . there is relatively low representation of items such as discussion of the clinical impression, the patient's affect, optimal intellectual functioning, etiology, the patient's dependency-independency status, his goals, and case history data . . . [pp. 218–221].

One should be aware that these conclusions are based on *spontaneous* suggestions of *some* psychiatrists, social workers, and psychologists. The conclusions could not and should not be used as general policy for all report writers, nor do the researchers intend them as such.

I have frequently pointed out that a report should meet the needs of the reader and should therefore be written from the reader's orientation. Often, however, though the reader's professed needs are very simple, the reporter collects a great deal of data which are beyond the immediate needs of the reader. The problem is what to do with the additional information. The problem has two facets: there is test or interview *data* which the reader has not asked for, and there are *interpretations* by the clinicians which have not been requested by the reader. Numerous examples come to mind for both facets. My students, for example, test clients of a reading and study center. The director of the center originally asked only for the intelligence quotient of the client. An hour spent testing a patient provides considerably more information than an IQ. Aware of some of the other needs of the director, I asked my students to write a longer report. The director now wants this information and states that he was unaware that such information was so readily available.

The question of providing unrequested interpretations or recommendations is a more complex one. If you have an interpretation of the relationship between patient and therapist, and the therapist has not asked for it, do you write it in a report? If you have an unrequested therapeutic recommendation, do you give it? This problem exists only when there are misunderstandings between professional workers. There are individual workers who feel strongly about their role and resent another worker's encroachment on this role. Otherwise, between people who come to know and respect each other's areas of proficiency, there is a mutual respect without unnecessarily strict circumscribing of roles. With this respect there is also an encouragement of flexibility and exchange of views.

If you have information beyond what is requested, talk to your reader and attempt to come to some understanding about the extent of your reports. Your reader may be unaware that you can provide some kind of information he needs; he may want your views on subjects not normally included in your reports. If specific instructions are lacking when preparing a report, the best rule to follow is this: write all you know rather than take the chance of leaving out exactly what is most needed.

The above discussion introduces a question all students ask: How long should the report be? There are as many answers to this as there are questions asked by the readers and institutions for which reports are written. Foster (1951) says that only the rare *psychological* report requires more than one typewritten page. He undoubtedly derived this rule from the specific setting in which he works. If there is a rule, it is that the length of a report depends on what needs to be said.

TEACHER OR REPORTER? "Teaching" the reader is inappropriate in a psychological report. Students have a penchant for adding sentences or paragraphs from textbooks on psychiatry, psychological theory, child development, and other fields. Their intent is to "back up" what they are saying about the patient. The extra material usually constitutes a prelude to a statement about the patient. Paragraphs are apt to begin: "Children of age four are expected to . . . ," "Symptoms of the obsessive-compulsive reaction are . . . ," and so on. These statements give a didactic flavor to the report, sound pedantic, and take the reader's mind off the patient. A compromise is accomplished by the following technique: "The patient shows these symptoms: . . . usually seen in an obsessive-compulsive reaction. Absent are the symptoms of . . . The fact that the patient does not show these latter symptoms may be accounted for on the following basis. . . ."

PHYSICAL DESCRIPTIONS OF THE PATIENT. The power of a physical description of a patient lies solely in the interpretive skill of the reporter. The question must always be: What value does this description have in promoting understanding of the patient?

Following are the kinds of descriptions which might have meaning in a report.

1. Some clinicians are specially trained to interpret *what the physique, stance, expression, etc., reveal about the patient.* These professionals usually have a particular orientation to interpretation of behavior not common to all of us. To them the patient's body is like a verbal response to a test question.

   This 25-year-old male patient is tall and thin. His continuously shifting eyes and his crouched body give the impression that he is awaiting doom.

2. Important statements can be made about the *relationship between physique and body image.*

   The patient is a 40-year-old, short, muscular man with a broad face and broken nose—a prizefighter until three years before his admission to the hospital. His manner is that of an adolescent girl: his gait is mincing, his hands flutter, he giggled and flirted with the male examiner.

3. Some patients' physical appearance can be expected to have a *striking effect on other people.* This should always be included, especially if this effect can be shown to pertain to his relations with people or to any other aspect of his life. Examples are patients whose physical appearance is frightening, those who are unusually handsome, those who are unusually drab.

   The patient's mother is blonde, thin, expensively dressed, and taller than the average woman; she looks like a fashion model.

   If such things as beauty and drabness are to be noted, they should be carefully described. Particularly annoying descriptive words are those involving a value judgment of the vaguest nature and revealing nothing but the likes and dislikes of the clinician. The word *attractive,* for example, means nothing except attractive *to the writer.* To borrow an example from fiction, Tolstoy seldom if ever describes a woman as "beautiful" or "attractive"; instead he describes other people's reactions to her.

4. Some patients appear obviously quite *different from the way they would "normally" be expected to appear.* Examples are the very thin person who has put on weight in some particular area of his body, the physically ill person, the person whose disheveled appearance is a reflection of his present reaction to the stress he is undergoing.

If the reporter can produce none of these descriptions, the physical description should be very brief, included only as data for the reader to interpret as he sees fit. If the reporter cannot write a diagnostically helpful statement, then the "patient is a rosy-cheeked, freckled, chubby boy of 9 years" type of description will suffice. A longer and well-stated description can, on the other hand, characterize a patient just as does a quote.

DESCRIBING THE PATIENT'S BEHAVIOR IN THE CLINIC. Similar to physical descriptions, the patient's behavior during interview or testing is often not only boring but meaningless. Nonetheless, some description, probably no more than a sentence or two in length, should always be included. This is for the use of the reader, whether it has any meaning to the reporter or not. In some cases certain behavior may have no particular meaning to the reporter, but to the reader may be quite surprising and even bring forth an entirely new interpretation of the patient's personality. For example, the reader may always have seen the patient as a quiet, submissive person and find that during testing he was highly active, hostile, and verbal. This could seem "natural" to the reporter but surprising and very helpful to the reader. When the clinic behavior has special meaning to the rest of the report, the reporter may use more space to describe it.

In the one or two sentences used to describe behavior, the reporter should make an effort to write a word picture of a unique individual and not a description common to an entire class of people. Words or phrases used in every report by a writer should probably be eliminated from his vocabulary. Many of us have a habit of writing, "The patient was cooperative." This is an example of stereotypy which could be shifted to a more interesting description of the patient's actual behavior.

The following kinds of behavioral descriptions can be very meaningful.

1. The interview or test behavior which *epitomizes the personality* as you perceive it. If the patient writes the report for you through his behavior or verbalizations, let him. His posture, the expression on his face, a gesture, a test response may be described in one succinct sentence to give the essence of the person.

2. Behavioral responses to *particular interview or test stimuli.* A patient may respond similarly to all tests except one, all interview questions except one, all Rorschach cards except one. This one exception may show an entirely new side of the patient. Whatever it is, it should be reported. On occasion, the exception may be so different from other behavior that the clinician cannot "fit it in" or interpret it. In every case the behavior should be mentioned.

3. Striking *reactions to the interviewer's age, sex, manner,* etc. This is, of course, noted to be striking only if the interviewer knows that the patient's accustomed behavior is different with people other than the interviewer. For example, the child with a behavior problem who "acts up" in school with

older female teachers may be quiet and cooperative with a young male examiner. This kind of notation may have dynamic and even prognostic value.

QUOTES FROM THE PATIENT. Some reports can be written at least in part by the patient himself. An exciting thing in both testing and therapy is the quote from the patient which epitomizes all or part of his life situation. When I get such a quote I can be sure it states the situation more succinctly and dramatically than I could state it. The following use of patients' statements illustrates how these statements may be used in a report.

> The patient's life has been completely taken over by the mother. He sees her as having "caught him," "held him," "tied him"—"that animal that catches you by his hands and holds you" (crab).
>
> "I feel weighted down, as if someone were sitting on my shoulders, and I had the responsibility for carrying them the rest of my life."
>
> In general, he sees women as prostitutes, inferior beings. The threat the female offers prevents his establishing any lasting relationship—"I get up, say thank you very much, pay the money, and leave."
>
> "In the dream an older man, nine feet tall, came toward me. He had a large knife and he knew what I was thinking although I didn't. I covered my head. It doesn't make sense, but I'm very depressed by it."

WHAT TO DO WITH TEST DATA. Psychology students often quote specialized test data in support of their interpretations. Some psychological reports are replete with sentences like

> His use of color (M:C = 0:9) is indicative of lability and an extremely narcissistic character (FC:CF:C = 1:1:5.)

Few readers want to know the data from which interpretations are made. Exceptions to this, such as quoting the patient when the quote reveals some unique characteristic, have been noted previously.

There are other exceptions. It is appropriate to give specialized test data to a reader who is known to be a specialist in the kinds of data being used. In this case the reporter should simply ask the reader if he wants the data. For example, a person highly experienced with the Strong Vocational Interest Blank may wish the actual scores along with the interpretations. Some Rorschach specialists want scores included, either in the body of the report or in an addendum.

You can answer the question Do I or do I not include test data? by simply asking the reader if and in what form he wants them. If they are not requested, leave them out. For many readers they produce nothing but confusion.

THE IMPRESSIONS OF COLLABORATING PROFESSIONALS. Previous diagnostic or other professional opinions should be noted and commented on by report writers. The writer should deny previous opinions, confirm them, note contraindications, or at least make some statement which reflects that he has considered the matter. This may be done in the following ways:

> While the psychiatrist reports . . . , the patient's behavior with this examiner was markedly different in the following ways: . . . .
>
> The diagnosis of . . . made by the intake worker is contraindicated by the results of psychological testing.
>
> The impressions of this therapist confirm the intake diagnosis of. . . .

IF YOU CANNOT INTERPRET WHAT YOU HAVE. Obtaining data which cannot be interpreted by the reporter is not uncommon, even to the highly skilled clinician. An odd response, a peculiar pattern of statements, or a bizarre figure drawing are often like an article of clothing which "does not belong" on a particular person. The behavior bears no relation to the person as you see him. An added problem may be that you cannot recall any reference to this kind of response in any of your training.

In reporting to another professional, this data should always be included (if it is appropriate to the function of the report). To delete what you do not understand may do both the patient and your reader a disservice, since the data may be of crucial importance to the case. Data can have meaning to your reader because of his particular training in a special area or his additional knowledge of the patient, while you may have neither of these.

Such information can be handled simply with a statement such as, "While the examiner cannot interpret this behavior, the patient displayed. . . ." Stating what you do not know is no reflection on your skill as a clinician; deleting your lack of knowledge is a reflection on your skill as a reporter.

VI. HOW TO PUT IT IN WRITING

Beginning in grade school, report writers in psychology and psychiatry take courses in the use of the English language. An exhaustive discussion of this subject is therefore not appropriate here. For reference, you may wish to study Hammond and Allen's book (1953) on English usage and report writing. Books specifically on word usage have been compiled by Fowler (1950), Nicholson (1957), and Evans and Evans (1957).

The following suggestions relate directly to the special problems encountered in report writing.

WHAT NOT TO DO. Merrill (1947) gives the following advice:

> To do a consistently poor job . . . one must grasp a few essential principles:
>
> I. Ignore the reader.
> II. Be verbose, vague, and pompous.
> III. Do not revise.

Practice a dead-pan technique, keeping your facts and ideas all on the same level of emphasis with no telltale hints of relative importance or logical sequence. . . . Write hurriedly, preferably when tired. Have no plan; write down items as they occur to you. The article will thus be spontaneous and poor. Hand in your manuscript the moment it is finished [p. 72].

This almost completely covers the mechanics of bad report writing. What follows is simply an expansion of the converse of these few principles.

LUCIDITY AND SUBTLETY. An initial error students make is the attempt to be subtle. Many people attracted to the behavioral professions have had at some time the desire to write fiction. To the frustrated fiction writer, subtlety is an attraction. He decides to use subtlety in his reports as he would use it in a piece of fiction. Report writing, however, is not the same as fiction writing. The difference lies in the response produced in the reader. Fiction is sometimes judged as good in proportion to the amount the reader can project, "read into," develop his own interpretation of the story. In fiction there is pleasure, too, simply in the words themselves.

Report writing is quite another matter. Words for their own sake are inappropriate in clinical reports. Even more important: the reader should not be "left on his own"; there should be no place for him to "read into" the report. He should be informed explicitly; he should know exactly what the reporter means. The statements in a report are apt to influence the reader greatly in making important decisions about a patient's life. These statements should therefore be clear and unequivocal.

One of my students had worked for some years in a literary office. Subtlety was at a premium in this setting and had become for him a thing in itself, one of his pleasures in communication. In describing a child who had been tested in numerous clinics, the student had a totally new interpretation of the child's behavior. He wished to show in the report that previous diagnoses and descriptions were misinterpretations of the child's behavior. He accomplished this, he thought, by devoting a long paragraph completely to quotes from previous reports. What he left out was any explanation of why he included these quotes. He had given careful thought to this procedure and decided that no comment was necessary, that to quote without comment was subtle. The difficulty was that the reader could have come to numerous conclusions from the presence of these unexplained quotes in the report.

A report is no place for subtlety. What you report about a patient is too important to risk being misunderstood.

CLARITY AND SIMPLICITY. A difficult thing to learn in the initial stages of report writing is the knack of writing in a clear, simple, straightforward way. In learning to write reports, students often use sentences which are complex, very professional sounding, and utterly confusing. Early in the course of supervision, the supervisor may question many sentences of a report and ask what the student is really trying to say. Changing his set by being required to state the idea orally, the student can usually rephrase it in a clear and simple statement.

Often confusion arises because sentences are too long. Strunk and White's (1959) advice is: "Clarity, clarity, clarity. When you become hopelessly mired in a sentence, it is best to start fresh; do not try to fight your way through against the terrible odds of syntax. Usually what is wrong is that the construction has become too involved at some point; the sentence needs to be broken apart and replaced by two or more shorter sentences" (p. 65).

One psychologist of my acquaintance teaches all of his students that the best reports consist of three-word sentences.

While this advice is an exaggeration, it nevertheless points a direction worth following. Occasionally long sentences are necessary. Long sentences serve the sole purpose of keeping one complex idea in one box between periods, when breaking it into two sentences would weaken it.

The danger of complex or overly long sentences is that the reader may be stopped by them. If you stop the reader, you lose him. This occurs quite subtly. He reads a sentence which he does not understand, and then scans two or three more sentences but does not actually read them because he is working on the confusing sentence. If he is confused enough, he can miss a great deal of what you are saying. If he stops to reread a sentence, he loses to some extent the gestalt of the report.

Readers have neither the time nor the inclination to study a report as they would study a textbook. Readers of reports about people can be expected to be careful but not studious. The trick for the writer to learn is to write so that a careful reader will understand what he is reading.

Some ways to avoid difficult writing: read your report aloud, read it as if you were your supervisor, read it as if you were the recipient of the report, or read it with a friend. The point is to get some perspective on your report regardless of how you do it. Any method of seeing the report as others see it will help you make it clearer.

QUALIFIERS AND INDECISION. The following is a list of words which can be counted on to weaken your writing, show your indecision, and cause your reader to think twice before giving any weight to what you say:

may be	seems to	suggests
might be	it is believed	apparently
appears to		

When you are so indecisive as to use two of these in the same sentence, you can be sure you are writing poorly. In a study of seven reports written by seven psychologists, I found a range of seven to fifteen qualifying phrases used within the confines of a page-and-a-half report. For example, the sentence

> The patient *appears to be* experiencing a conflict *perhaps* engendered by a traumatic rejection by the mother and *what seems to be* a need to be loved and protected by her.

should be stated in the following way:

> The patient *is* experiencing a conflict engendered by a traumatic rejection by the mother and a need to be loved and protected by her.

A simple way to check the tendency to qualify is to read your report and eliminate every qualifier. After reading it over, there may be qualifiers you wish to retain. Put them in again if they are needed and if the qualification is clear.

As a professional you are asked for a professional *opinion.* Clinical reports are by no means the "truth" or the final word about a patient. As stated previously, reports are at best one clinician's perception of another human being. There is therefore no reason to say "the patient appears to be"; from the clinician's point of view, "the patient *is.*" A report full of qualifiers leaves the reader wondering what the reporter really thought.

There is one exception to what has been said. This occurs when the reporter has very slim evidence, but the possible implications of this evidence are so important as to demand inclusion. For example:

> The patient may have an alcoholic problem. While in the five tests administered there was only one response

suggestive of alcoholism, the therapist should entertain this possibility.

Some writers are addicted to a special form of qualification, reflected in such terms as *very excellent* or *very brilliant*. These are redundant, not unlike saying "the most best" or "a very intelligent genius."

Qualification involving quantity[1] is a tricky problem. Quantity qualifiers commonly used in reports are the following:

somewhat	a degree of	generally
extremely	quite	at times
too often	marked	some
very	not wholly	fairly

A simple rule on the use of qualifiers: qualify when you intend to do just that, but be sure your meaning is clear. For example, "There is a fair degree of hostility toward authority figures, i.e., enough to prevent him from keeping a job for any protracted period but not enough to cause violent behavior." This illustrates the best solution to quantity qualification: Make your statement in behavioral terms.

QUALIFICATION AND VALUE JUDGMENTS. Anyone who saw the motion picture *Rashomon* will recall the brilliant exposition of four people's perceptions of a single incident witnessed by all of them. The extreme difference in the four stories was remarkable in its revelation of how the needs and values of the perceiver affect his perception. As psychiatrists and psychologists, we are all familiar with this phenomenon. We do, however, sometimes forget that our value judgments in clinical work may not be the same as our reader's, and therefore we may not be communicating well with terms of value judgment.

[1] See American Psychiatric Association, *Diagnostic and Statistical Manual: Mental Disorders*, Washington, 1952, pp. 44, 47–49.

Especially vague are terms like *good, well, poor,* and *adequate.* In industrial reports, for example, the conclusion that a candidate will be a "good" manager is extremely vague unless the writer and reader agree on what a good manager is. Even if there is agreement, the writer will do well to spell out exactly how the candidate fits the specifications. A particular shortcoming exists when we say that someone will be "good" in a job the specifications of which we do not even know clearly. Before any such terms are employed, the writer should satisfy himself that the reader will be able to answer the question: Good, poor, or adequate in relation to what?

A good rule: When a report is finished, go over every word of value judgment to see that (1) it is essential, and (2) its meaning will be completely clear to the reader.

JARGON. According to English and English (1958) jargon is a language peculiar to a particular trade, profession, or other group. When a profession develops jargon, the jargon serves only one useful function. It becomes a shorthand, a method of stating briefly what would take much longer to state without the jargon.

When the report writer uses jargon, the important requirement to keep in mind is that the reporter and the reader use the same jargon or shorthand. If the writer uses Gregg shorthand and the reader knows only Pitman, some confusion will arise.

Very few ingroup terms can take the place of behavioral descriptions and meaningful psychological interpretations written in simple, down-to-earth language.

Some clinicians use phrases like "the patient is fixated at the oral stage" with no further explanation. This leaves a great deal to the imagination of the reader. The reader's interpretation of what this means about the patient may be totally different from what the reporter has in mind.

W. G. Klopfer (1960) has illustrated very well the possibilities of restating technical language. For example, he suggests the following replacement for the expression *oedipal involvement:*

The patient has always had a very close relationship with his mother. Her own feelings toward him being mixed, she has alternately bound him to her with an excessive display of affection and made him insecure within the relationship by rejection and coyness. The fact that the patient has not been able to resolve this relationship has made it very difficult for him to look upon other women objectively and to relate to them in a mature and rational manner. Also, his great involvement with his mother, who has often used him as a medium through which to express mixed feelings toward the father, has distorted his relationship with men so that they are often seen as rivals rather than allies [p. 2].

This appears to be, of course, a very long statement to replace two words. It is obviously written, however, to describe one particular patient's "oedipal involvement." The statement, while long, is very clear. This quote illustrates how easily a technical term could be misinterpreted if not explained clearly. The use of "oedipal involvement" could be interpreted in many ways. Klopfer has obviously employed the concept in his thinking but applies it individually, demonstrating a particular variation on a theme. If a report writer assumes "oedipal involvement" in everyone, then the use of the term without explanation is meaningless.

Some jargon is perfectly appropriate. There are some in-group terms which are understandable to all professionals and have only one meaning. Hammond and Allen (1953, pp. 232–233) list a group of words commonly known in the clinical professions; they include certain medical and psychological concepts not ordinarily used by laymen. Examples: coitus, syndrome, trauma, petit mal, conditioning, dissociation. There is little or no question as to the meaning of these words.

"Anxiety," on the other hand, has been said to have 61 meanings.

Mayman (1959, p. 457) lists a group of terms which have invited criticism. He suggests that they bear close scrutiny before we use them.

impulsive
malignant
hysteriform
decompensating
impulse-ridden
psychotic character
strong oral-aggressive drive
identification with the aggressor
compulsivity
narcissistic
ego strength
schizophrenic
phobic tendencies
projective mechanisms
strong depressive features

Terms like *shallow affect, flat affect,* and *inappropriate affect* present a problem. The questions these terms evoke from students are: Inappropriate to what? How shallow is shallow? How flat is flat? What does flat mean? Both shallow and flat are physical analogies; analogies, while dramatic, are dangerously open to misinterpretation.

If the writer has any question about the meaning of a term, he should consult the excellent dictionary of psychological and psychoanalytical terms by English and English (1958). This dictionary not only defines words but discusses difficulties with certain terms and the history of their usage.

Nothing takes the place of description and interpretation stated in simple and behavioral terms. Jargon should be used only if the words communicate clearly and meaningfully to the reader what the reporter wishes to say.

PET IDEAS AND PHRASES. Many of us are wedded to one or more special ideas or concepts. A psychologist may, for example, always mention the level of "rigidity" of every patient. Rigidity is at best a vague concept; the use of such a concept is appropriate only when defined and when it is a notable symptom of the patient. Noting the *lack* of rigidity is like noting the lack of eleven fingers.

The repetitive use of one idea in reports produces nothing but dullness, skipping, and lack of attention by the reader, particularly the reader who must regularly read the reports of one writer. It is apt to result from boredom with report writing, lack of imagination, lack of understanding of the patient, and, in some cases, the personal problems of the writer.

Regarding pet phrases, the safest rule is to eliminate any phrasing of which you are particularly fond or which seems unusually clever to you. You can be fairly certain that it is overly personal, "tricky," or simply does not communicate anything.

STEREOTYPY. Closely related to pet ideas is the problem of stereotypy of reports. I have often heard the complaint, "Dr. S.'s reports all sound alike." If you are accused of stereotypy, the thing to do is read over your reports to see what has gone wrong. The questions you might ask of yourself are: Is this report essentially like the one I wrote yesterday and the day before and the day before that? Could this report depict not only this patient but all people as well?

A psychologist related the following incident which would be amusing if it were not such an alarming commentary on some kinds of report writing. Working in a mental hospital, he offered to write a psychological report for a fellow psychologist. As his data for the report he took only the age and sex of the patient and produced a full-length psychological report. It consisted only of clichés that could be used to describe any person of that age and sex, or indeed of almost anyone: "The patient is experiencing passive-aggressive problems reflected in dependent behavior at one time and hostile, aggressive actions at other times. . . . The patient will respond well to therapeutic endeavors depending on the relationship established between him and the therapist." The psychologist's report was read in case conference and was accepted without comment from the staff. The fact that there was no comment may well signify that the staff was accustomed to cliché reports and no comment was necessary. This is true in many settings and explains why both report writing and report reading *can be* boring and meaningless.

SOME MECHANICAL MINUTIAE. I have specifically avoided any long discussions of English grammar and mechanics common to all writing. There are, however, two common practices which produce unpleasant reading. These practices are the use of contractions and the use of hyphens.

Students often use contractions in an effort to make a report seem natural, the way the student would speak. The written word, however, produces a completely different effect from the same word when spoken. Contractions on paper are apt to appear strange to the reader, seem flippant, and for both these reasons disturb the reader. The following is an example:

> This child can't tolerate frustration of any kind. He doesn't know how to handle it and hasn't developed consistent methods for avoiding it.

Contractions seem to some students to bring simplicity and lack of affectation. The fact is that they bring neither. A report is a formal statement, not a quote from a novel. Contractions should be used *only when quoting the patient*, if this is the way he speaks.

Writers suffering from hyphenitis produce pages which look very much like a speckled hen. The hyphens most of us use are totally unnecessary. Referring to Fowler (1950), Nicholson (1957), or Evans and Evans (1957) is the simplest, safest, and quickest solution to the question of hyphen or no hyphen. If this seems too time consuming, the best rule is to eliminate the hyphen and see whether the meaning is quite clear without it.

STYLE. There are two excellent books concerning style in writing. One is by Strunk and White, *The Elements of Style* (1959). The other is Ferguson's *Say It With Words* (1959).

Report writing is to some degree an art in the sense that the writer's personality and outlook are imposed on the data he is observing. Style of writing is one of the means by which a writer imposes his personality on a report. To *attempt* style, however, is risky. Strunk and White's advice is this:

> The beginner should approach style warily, realizing that it is himself he is approaching, no other; and he should begin by turning resolutely away from all devices that are popularly believed to indicate style—all mannerisms, tricks, adornments. The approach to style is by way of plainness, simplicity, orderliness, sincerity. . . . the first piece of advice is this: to achieve style, begin by affecting none—that is, place yourself in the background. A careful and honest writer does not need to worry about style [pp. 55–56].

Thus, write in a way that is your own. You can enrich your writing by reading the reports of other writers whom you admire and by talking to your reader. This does not mean that you are becoming someone else; you are simply picking up what would have been yours all along if you had known about it. You should resist anyone's imposing a style on you. During your training days, you will hopefully have supervision, but it is not your supervisor's task or right to insist on a style of writing that is not yours. When you develop a real style to your writing, it will come from you.

VII. THE DILEMMA OF CONFIDENTIALITY

Reports in psychiatry and psychology are written almost without exception to communicate information which is extremely confidential. The information often includes the most intimate details—the overt and covert actions and innermost thoughts and wishes—of another human being. Perhaps even more important is this: what you write about people can often profoundly help their careers or damage their future. For these reasons the question of confidentiality is an extremely serious one.

If there is any one rule on the issue of confidentiality, it is to ask yourself: What will my recording this information do to the patient? Asking this question will sometimes clarify and simplify the dilemma. The question, however, is and will always be unanswerable except by an individual in a particular situation at a particular time. And you can never be sure that your solution is the right one.

The reason the question of confidentiality is always complex is that if the question arises in the first place, there are important and contradictory responsibilities at stake. In essence, you are usually weighing your responsibility to the patient, to your own organization, and to society.

Menninger (1952, pp. 40–42) offers some principles regarding the problem: ". . . the honest fulfillment of responsibility to all parties will be of the greatest benefit to each of them"; the clinician should "so couch the material in his clinical history that innocent parties do not suffer, and this includes the patient"; the clinician "who takes the record should have it very much on his conscience that he is responsible for the extent of dissemination of the information." Menninger's first principle is simply a restatement of the problem, and the question remains, How does one do this? The second gives at least a partial answer to the question. The third is an ethical principle which, if not followed, should exclude a person from clinical professions. These quotes illustrate that helpful advice on this question is slim. Every occupation has its risks; this is one in the mental health professions.

The dilemma of confidentiality is exemplified in the following situation. A psychiatric resident was asked to examine an obstetrical patient who had requested an interview with a psychiatrist. The patient's symptoms included severe depression at the death of her infant. During the interview, the patient extracted a vague promise from the momentarily indecisive resident that he would not divulge anything to the obstetrician. The patient then gave a long and extremely confidential history, including her extramarital sexual promiscuity, all unknown to her obstetrician; her story explained her depression quite fully. The resident wrote the entire history in the chart, knowing this procedure was a hospital rule. For the next week the question of whether or not he should have recorded this information plagued him. In recommending the patient to the resident, the obstetrician had specifically asked only if the patient was suicidal; the obstetrician was apparently neither psychologically trained nor interested in personality dynamics.

This story illustrates a conflict of responsibilities: to the patient, to the referring physician, to the hospital, and to some future clinic or hospital where the patient might be treated. Add to this some illegal activity or proposed behavior which might endanger another person, and you have the gamut of problems.

The American Psychological Association (1953) has published ethical standards on the problem of confidentiality which are well worth the consideration of all people in the helping professions:

> The psychologist's ultimate allegiance is to society, and his professional behavior should demonstrate an awareness of his social responsibilities. The welfare of the profession and of the individual psychologist are clearly subordinate to the welfare of the public. In nearly all circumstances, the welfare of the public, of the profession, and of the individual psychologist can best be served by placing highest value on the immediate responsibility of the psychologist [p. 7].

> The psychologist should guard professional confidences as a trust and reveal such confidences only after most careful deliberation and when there is clear and imminent danger to an individual or to society [p. 55].

> The psychologist should give clinical information about a client only to those persons whom the client might reasonably be expected to consider a party to the psychologist's effort to help him. The client's concurrence should be obtained before there is any communication exceeding these customary limits [p. 63].

In writing reports on your patients, two rules may help guide you:

1. Obtain the patient's permission to write the report. The safest way is to have him sign a release slip.

2. Discuss with the patient what you are going to write. This procedure has even been found, in some cases, to be therapeutic.

For reports of all kinds, the following statements may act as a guide:

1. Be specific. Vague statements protect you but not the patient. The vaguer the statement, the more the reader can make incorrect, and perhaps harmful, interpretations.
2. Write a frank report when you are describing psychotic or dangerous anticipated behavior or the behavior of a minor. In none of these cases can you get permission from the patient. Naturally, one must consider who is getting the report, what level of understanding he has, and what he can be expected to do with the information. The fundamental point here is the danger to society.
3. If there is a single guiding principle, it is that if you have respect for the patient and your relationship with him is good, the letter or report you write will probably be appropriate and unharmful to him. But this is no guarantee.

The endless question of how to handle confidential information can be solved to some degree by our constantly reminding ourselves of the limitations of our professional knowledge. We must also recognize that we cannot know or foresee all circumstances relating to a patient. Humility is some safeguard. But unfortunately the major safeguard lies in the morality and human decency of the report writer himself.

VIII. SOME EXAMPLES OF REPORT WRITING

Some examples of report writing other than those already quoted will illustrate some of the points made in this book. Quoting only parts of some reports, it is hoped, will do violence neither to the complete reports nor to the sensitivities of the writers.

Example **A**

Case 99. Vocational Suitability; Question of "Hereditary Taint"

Report to: ______ Missionary Board
Subject: Mr. W. H. H.
Summary of: Psychiatric report

......

Psychiatric Status

The candidate possesses a superior and versatile intelligence, with special capacities in abstract thought, inductive reasoning and facility of symbolic and verbal communication. In personality he is honest, frank,

sincerely friendly, and capable of deep emotional empathies. For instance, he has quite plausibly reconstructed the possible causes of his mother's psychosis from her own early upbringing and her later marital and familial frustrations and conflicts. He is no longer troubled by tendencies toward introspection or fantasy and his interpersonal relationships are relatively wholesome and constructive. His motivations toward missionary work, though of course comprised in part of his own diverse seekings for powers and securities, are neither fanatically grandiose nor escapist, and should prove reliable and productive.

Recommendations

No evidence was elicited to prejudice Mr. H.'s fitness for missionary work; on the contrary, we are happy to recommend him as well qualified by intelligence, personality and motivation for his projected tasks.

Parenthetically, there is at present no incontrovertible proof that any form of functional psychosis is transmitted from generation to generation except by early environmental influences [Masserman, 1955, p. 271].

COMMENTS

1. The last paragraph illustrates the textbook teaching referred to previously. Even in this instance it is probably inappropriate. By logic, however, one does wonder whether the reader might safely conclude that the candidate is indeed a candidate for psychotic reaction on the basis of "the early environmental influence" of a psychotic mother. Since the candidate was interviewed initially because of question of "hereditary taint," the conclusion might better have been, "There is no evidence that Mr. H. will develop a psychotic reaction," if this is what the writer believed.

   As stated previously, clinical reports are no place for didactic generalizations, especially of a highly controversial nature. The cumbersome quality of "no incontrovertible proof" demonstrates the difficulty of stating this complex idea simply. The reader wants a professional opinion about a person, not a lecture on psychiatry.

2. While the psychiatric status is fairly easy to read, the ingroup lingo is inappropriate and clouds the report. *Symbolic communication, emotional empathies, grandiose,* and *escapist* are all terms which warrant some definition for the lay reader. Even *inductive reasoning, introspection,* and *fantasy* are questionable concepts in a report to the layman. In each case simple words might have been substituted.
3. If the subject is "no longer troubled by . . . ," why mention his previous difficulties? This is often a reflection of the writer's uncertainty concerning whether these behaviors might recur without his actually taking responsibility for stating a definite opinion. Carrying this practice to an extreme, we would be forced to mention all of the previous maladaptive responses of the patient.
4. One questions two things about the "for instance." What is its referrant, and what does it illustrate? Also, in a report of such brevity, why is an example necessary?

Example B

S engages in liberated creative imagination. He reacts to his world with vigorous feeling experiences. He is also entirely realistic, and his intelligence is at the most superior level. Broad cultural influences molded him. Still, there are low lights in this bright picture. He is not altogether smooth in his intellectual procedures; he suffers from some feelings of inferiority; anxiety holds him in rein; the inevitable neurosis is present. In a word, he represents one of the directing class of our time, yet is revealed as all too human . . . [Beck, 1947, pp. 63–64].

COMMENTS

This is Beck's opening paragraph (and summary) of his well-known Rorschach report on a college president.

1. There is an obvious style and poetic flavor to the writing. This kind of writing is striking and interesting, but is apt to

cause the reader to begin analyzing the writer rather than think about the patient.

2. The long sentence separated by semicolons is a good example of one thought with many parts boxed in a long sentence. The thought and the strength of the writing would suffer if separated into parts.
3. ". . . the inevitable neurosis is present" is Beck's conclusion to his long sentence. This is the kind of revelation of a theoretical position which is apt to tell more about the writer than the subject. Thus it shifts attention from the subject to the writer. Beck's implied concept that we are all neurotic (if this is what he means) is so personal that it warrants exclusion.

Example C

His oral needs are very pronounced, manifesting themselves in a need for acquisition of money and fame. . . . He sees the paternal figure as aggressive and depriving. Contemporary male figures are seen as competitive and there is a strong homosexual interest in them. Maternal figures are seen with considerable ambivalence and guilt over his aggressive feelings toward them, and also with strong oral demands toward them . . . [Bellak, 1954, p. 87].

COMMENTS

1. This is an example of a report written from a particular theoretical frame of reference. While many clinicians are familiar with Freudian theory, there is some doubt that the mention of orality would be understood by all readers. It is mentioned not once but twice, and the meaning of the paragraph to some extent stands or falls on a full comprehension of what the writer means. Obviously, unless the reader is known fully to understand and appreciate the writer's theoretical orientation, such terms are to be avoided.

2. The use of such verb structures as "are seen" is apt to produce numerous complications, as this does here. One must read the sentence at least twice to catch its meaning. The last sentence might be clarified and strengthened in this way: He is ambivalent toward maternal figures and feels guilty about his aggressive feelings toward them. He also makes strong demands on them.

Example D

In summary, . . . this is a naive, egocentric, repressive, narcissistic woman with significant feelings of smallness and inadequacy. She appears to try to view herself as a fair, innocent, virginal damsel in distress who needs somewhat depreciated and sexless but attentive beaux to admire her and minister to her, and who also needs a hero to save her. Also suggested is noteworthy anxiety over physical status, aging, infirmity and death, particularly that of the male figure but possibly her own as well. A phobic trend may also be present [Schafer, 1954, pp. 201–202].

COMMENTS

1. The opening sentence with the list of adjectives is used by many writers and usually serves the purpose of summarizing the patient's personality in one sentence.
2. The use of the words "she appears to," "also suggested," and "may also be present" leaves some question as to the writer's certainty about what he is saying. Since the summary is only four sentences long, and three of them begin with qualifying terms, the strength of the summary is cut down considerably.
3. His use of "significant feelings of" and "noteworthy anxiety" leaves the reader wondering why the writer qualifies in this way. The patient's feelings must be significant and her anxiety noteworthy or the writer would have eliminated both from his report. In general, as noted elsewhere,

qualifications about the patient's behavior, etc., should be used sparingly.

4. ". . . particularly that of the male figure . . ." is an example of the kind of statement which is apparently completely clear to the writer and totally unclear to the reader. Even after rereading the phrase (which the reader should not be required to do) one wonders to what it refers—does it refer to the anxiety, or to one of the list of anxiety producers, or only to death? This kind of confusion may be avoided, as noted previously, by reading the report aloud or attempting to imagine the recipient's reading it.
5. "She appears to try to view herself as . . ." is a very confusing statement. This kind of confusion may be avoided by being explicit, e.g., "With men, she behaves as if . . . ; while with women, she . . . ," or "While she behaves as . . . , her fantasies are . . . ," or "While she behaves as a . . . , she would like to. . . ."

Example E

This competent, energetic, self-confident Sergeant is very well qualified for his assignment by his ability, personality, and background. He is a determined, clear-thinking person who has well-defined values and goals which he pursues with unswerving persistence, fully utilizing his capacity for hard work. In spite of his pronounced tendency toward self-reliance and independence which, combined with his rejection of indiscriminate gregariousness, often leads to bluntness in social relations, he is essentially a person of good will, is frank, sympathetic, sincere, and a good mixer. While his brusqueness and independence may alienate people upon first contact, over a longer period of time the student is likely to win and hold both the respect and the affection of his colleagues. These traits, together with his readiness to take responsibilities for others, to solve problems, and to make decisions, qualify the candidate for a position of leadership higher than one that would be compatible with his rank.

Son of a successful attorney-at-law, the candidate grew up in Oregon

and Wisconsin and from an early age developed a great love for outdoor life, becoming proficient in mountain climbing, skiing, riding, and swimming. He was always a good student in school, sociable and active in a variety of extracurricular pursuits. Very close to both parents, and admiring of his father's character and achievements, he decided to follow him in the legal profession, and obtained his degree from the University of Missouri in 1941. Expecting to be drafted, he postponed going into practice, and took a job with the U.S. Department of Justice. He enjoyed this work greatly, and in the course of it has acquired some experience in questioning Chinese and Japanese. Inducted into the Army in 1943, he went through basic training and a radio school and has worked as a radio instructor for the last two years. In spite of slow promotion, he has adjusted well to this situation, has enjoyed teaching, for which he obtained the highest ratings, and has utilized his free time for extensive reading in the field of law and social sciences. He wants an overseas assignment because he feels that he should do more for the war effort and feels capable of handling a strenuous and responsible mission. Although the candidate's strong desire to do well makes him nervous and tense in test situations, or in beginning a new type of work, increasing familiarity with the situation quickly dissolves these tensions; the student is well integrated emotionally and has no disturbing conflicts or fears; while he does not seek danger he is willing to take any risks that the assignment might involve.

This candidate was very highly motivated for all of the situations at S. He entered into the assignments enthusiastically and exerted himself to the utmost in order to achieve a successful solution of his group's problems. Possessing a good measure of forcefulness and self-assertiveness, he was usually the first to make any bid for leadership. Only the lack of sufficient ingenuity in field problems prevented him from carrying out this role with distinction. He is adaptable and flexible—attributes which should stand him in good stead in acquiring the leadership techniques and fundamental knowledge necessary to handle his projected assignment effectivly.

He has a strong desire to plan and carry out tasks on the basis of his own ideas. As a result, he tends to be somewhat abrupt with others who have different ideas and he is very likely to overlook their point of view in favor of his own. However, he has sufficient insight into himself so that this characteristic rarely becomes so dominant as to interfere markedly with his social relations. Furthermore, his good will, warmth, and sympathetic understanding of others become more obvious as time goes on. He should, therefore, wear well with any group with which he is associated over a long period of time.

In situations which he regarded as critical tests of his abilities, his tensions expressed themselves in profuse sweating and quivering limbs. He was aware of his uneasiness and discomfiture but controlled himself so well that he never became upset and never permitted his emotionality to interfere with the work at hand.

He is highly recommended for his proposed assignment overseas [O. S. S. Assessment Staff, 1948, pp. 209–210].

COMMENTS

This report is quoted in its entirety not only because it illustrates some interesting points about report writing, but also because it is very much like some reports written by psychiatrists and psychologists for industrial purposes.

1. It is written with simple, everyday language and is easy to read. There is not one word of psychological jargon (although this would not necessarily be expected since it only rarely discusses intrapsychic material).
2. It is an excellent example of a report written without subheadings. The report could easily have been divided with some conventional headings: testing behavior, personal background, personality description, and recommendations. While this kind of dividing may not have added measurably to the initial readability, later reference to it would have been made much easier.
3. The most surprising thing to consider, in the light of its easy flow, is its peculiar sequence: personality description, personal background, more personality description (in the same paragraph as background), test behavior, more personality description, more test behavior, and recommendations. The intermittent discussion of test behavior

has the effect of seeming to demonstrate characteristic behavior of the patient. If this is what the writer intended, it should have been expressed as such. The report might have been even easier to follow if its sequence had been more organized: test behavior, personal background, personality description, and recommendations.

4. Does the applicant actually speak Chinese or Japanese? One would assume so but cannot be sure. If this information were needed at some later date, it might be very time consuming to obtain.
5. There is a striking (and welcome) lack of qualification. At no point does the writer use a term like "seems to" or "might." He is obviously giving a professional opinion, and it is stated with assurance.

Example F

Formulation and Diagnostic Impression (New Form)

This fifteen-year-old girl began manifesting behavior which was distressing to herself at eleven years, distressing to the community at fourteen years. This was clearly a progression of symptoms with the basic pattern unaltered qualitatively, yet intensified and accelerated. Initially she showed a gradual personality change, ultimately a blatant psychosis.

A review of the material revealed an unplanned and most probably an unwanted child, born to parents whose own emotional instability was already evident. However, she was precocious in development of walking and talking, and has demonstrated a very high intellectual potential. This precocious development of ego functions could have been a factor in the predisposition of pathology.

Ego growth was hampered by an infantilizing and inconsistent mother, in a situation where the patient was the youngest child for eight years. The relationship with the mother was intensified by the father's absences and withdrawals. Later desertion by the father, when the patient was four years old, prevented normal oedipal-phase development and fostered pregenital fixations. Object choice was predominantly on a narcissistic basis; and in time of stress, sufficient regression occurred to lead to loss of differentiation between self and object representations.

Superego formation was similarly defective, a consequence of identification with an alcoholic delinquent father and a narcissistic mother, who utilized family members to fulfill her own instinctual wishes.

Instinctual drives were seemingly adequately controlled until the age of eleven years, when a personality change and the "secret life" started. This marked the onset of puberty with its attendant upsurge of id strivings, which required additional energy for control. The already weakened ego obviously had difficulty managing these increased demands. In addition, external factors, chaotic family circumstances, contributed toward further depletion of ego strength and enhancement of instinctual drives. As a result the ego was incapable of neutralizing the instinctual drives to a degree sufficient for adequate functioning.

With this psychic structure and constellation of circumstances, specific symptoms developed. The runaway symptom, which started at age thirteen, is reminiscent of her parents' marriages. Mother's first marriage was an elopement at sixteen years; the parental marriage (father's first and only, mother's second) were opposed by the paternal family. Fleeing from stress was a characteristic parental pattern, manifested by the mother in her withdrawal to poetry writing, and by the father in his solitary drinking and frequent departures. The patient's absences, initially secret, were associated with sexual activities with sailors and older men (brother and father surrogate; the teenage boys were sought much later, and during the psychotic episode). These absences originated during a period of enormous stress including the mother's hospitalization for the birth of the younger brother; a change in sixteen-year-old half sister Carry's behavior, wherein she assumed mother's role, wore mother's clothes, and imitated mother's behavior; the early arrival of the patient's menarche; the departure of seventeen-year-old half brother Bob, to become a sailor; the father's overt psychosis and removal to a sanitarium.

We remember that during the psychotic episode the patient stated, "My father raped me while my mother watched." The history also indicated that Ann watched while her father "molested" her older half sister (fact or fantasy); both situations probably indicate early and frequent observation of primal scenes and its traumatic effect. It may be speculated that this is one important factor in her confusion over sexuality, distorted self-image, and her bisexual identification.

It is significant that in the absence of external stress, in a structured, supportive, feminine environment, she behaved appropriately and func-

tioned well. This would indicate that this is an adolescent who is capable of borrowing ego strength for repression and adaptation.

Diagnostic Impression (New Form)

Schizophrenia with paranoid and catatonic elements [Fries and Friedman, 1960, pp. 36–40].

COMMENTS

This is a psychiatric "formulation and diagnostic impression" written for presentation to a supervisor (preceptor). The authors' intention was to illustrate the use of a new form for formulation. The authors recommend a thorough, unified, and chronological reporting method.

1. The formulation is purely chronological. The patient's behavior is shown to be related to her upbringing but also to her parents' own developmental history. The sequence is present, past, and future. The authors have chosen to bring in the parents and their past when this is appropriate to the description of some facet of the patient's development. The only use of "topics" or guides for the writer are those implicit in Freudian theory.
2. The use of the phrases "the . . . ego obviously had difficulty" and "the ego was incapable of" presents an interesting problem. This assigning of independent status to a "system" of the person is frequent in the writings of Freud. My own opinion is that in a report it is confusing and splits the person into parts even more than does a topical outline.
3. The report is replete with technical language. It was written for presentation to a preceptor and therefore we must assume the resident and the preceptor "speak the same language." Despite this, I believe the terms *ego functions, ego growth, oedipal-phase development,* and *pregential fixations* could be stated more simply and in behavioral fashion. The

student might find it an interesting exercise to attempt a restatement of paragraphs three and four in particular.

4. The diagnosis of "schizophrenia with paranoid and catatonic elements" in a psychiatric report written recently illustrates that the American Psychiatric Association manual (1952) is still not universally used.
5. The use of the expressions "probably" and "it may be speculated that" in the next to last paragraph are good illustrations of a writer's qualifying when he intended to do just that. As they are used here, these expressions give the reader the impression of no lack of decision on the part of the writer but rather a carefully considered speculation. While the writer uses some terms of quantity ("very high," "gradual," "blatant"), there is a remarkable lack of equivocation. Even in the use of the expression "most probably an unwanted child," the reader is left with the impression that the writer states things strongly when the opinion is clear, and at the same time offers important speculations and labels them as such.
6. The report is unusually well integrated. One clearly sees the central theme and its development. Furthermore, secondary themes are well integrated with the major interpretations or themes.

Example G[1]

Psychological Analysis

Intellectual Functioning

Mr. W. M. has very superior intelligence. He ranks in the upper 2 percent of the general population and well above the average of executive personnel. He is a man who likes to use his mind and is at almost all times putting forth maximum mental effort.

By endowment he has high verbal abilities; his mechanical-technical,

[1] Quoted by permission of Richardson, Bellows, Henry and Co., Inc.

non-verbal talents are not as impressive but still considerably above average. What high level talents he might lack in these latter fields, he makes up for by sheer effort. He has excellent learning ability and shows it in anything he undertakes.

He is capable of a very high-level performance in the verbal abstraction area. His abstract ability is also high in the non-verbal area. His fund of formal general knowledge is superior; his store of everyday information is very high. Mechanical information is only average. He is not quick with numbers, although he is above average in handling problems of an arithmetic nature. Here there is no great interest or talent and he must work at this to keep up with high level competition.

Relations with Others

He makes an excellent impression. He is a frank, direct person who enjoys human contact. His excellent knowledge of the formalities of human contact makes him an impressive representative of any group in any company. His own somewhat complex nature does not cause others to suffer; it does instead make him an interesting person to deal with.

He is extremely interested in people. This interest is not built on altruism or sympathy, but rather on the desire to understand others and to comprehend their motivations. This is both a kind of scientific curiosity and also the tool he uses to make the most of other people's talents and deal with them well. He is very objective in his evaluation of people in business.

He is an active, aggressive person. He places great stress on competence and is a taskmaster of both himself and others. Occasionally skeptical of the work of his subordinates, he keeps his finger on their activities. He is aware that he might overdo supervision, and is attempting to delegate authority more effectively. He takes a strong interest in the development of others.

He channels his emotions and warmth to very few people. To the rest of the world he shows courtesy and good manners. When annoyed he can become sarcastic and even harsh. This, however, is by no means out of control; when he displays his emotion he usually has a goal in mind.

His relations with superiors are adult. They come to know that he can be counted on with no need for constant advice or watching over.

Work Characteristics

He is a highly productive worker who also has high standards of quality. There is hardly any waste motion, though occasionally his moderate perfectionism leads him to expend energy on work which might well be done by others. His drive for quality does not end when the main job is done. He wants a "glossy finish" also.

He is a very hard worker, very much work oriented. He gives maximum effort at all times. He quickly grasps the main point and intent of a problem. Generally very well disciplined, he checks and re-checks facts as to their practicality. He has depth and originality. At times his critical approach and perfectionism limit the full force of his imagination.

A man of intellectual ambition, he does not stay satisfied for long with past achievement. Once a job becomes routine, he must move on to new problems in order to remain happy in his work life.

Aspirations and Drive

His drive is strong, well disciplined, and even. He has enormous energy and uses it well.

He has very high aspirations. He wants a top level position where he can use his creativity, where new problems are constantly presented, and where there is high responsibility. He has not settled in his own mind whether a staff or line position is best suited for him. The fact is that his talents, interests, and effort allow him to do almost everything well. In the past he has tended to allow his career to move according to the advice of respected superiors and what falls into his lap. While his highly varied moves have given him wide experience and perspective, he may soon have to make up his own mind where his talents may best be used for a terminal position.

Interests and Values

His two highest tested interests are in literary and scientific pursuits. His broad array of remaining interests illustates the fact that he can find interest in a great many things. His mental abilities and interests would not lead to the conclusion that he is a "born engineer" of the line variety, although again he could perform above average. His high verbal skills, his abstract ability, and his interests suit him for general management or a high level staff position.

His highest tested value is in theoretical matters. This is undoubtedly a reflection of his active, inquiring approach to life. Interested in everything, he deeply enjoys knowing the reasons behind things. He is also motivated by recognition, prestige, and position. Money also is valued but mostly as a sign of the above trinity. None of these would have meaning to him, however, without solid achievement. What he gets must be a reflection of what he has done.

His outside interests and activities cover a fairly wide range. They offer him relaxation, perspective, and richness in his development.

Family Background

His father was self-made, a hard worker, aggressive and perfectionistic. These qualities seem to have affected Mr. M. in a healthy rather than any restricting or crippling way.

He is married and has one son, age. . . . Not satisfied to allow his family life to stagnate or become routine, he constantly works to improve it and give it more meaning.

Personal Adjustment

He has a fundamentally good personal adjustment. Not impervious to emotional shocks, he, being a man of action, discharges his tension as he goes along. He may be expected continually to seek self-evaluation and self-impovement in a constructive way rather than in any involved, self-centered way. Although he is given to some inferiority feelings, his self-assurance and honesty are healthy. He is a man who is changing and growing continually. His superiors need have no hesitation to criticize him constructively; he will give it careful consideration and act on it.

Potential and Recommendation

Mr. W. M. is an unusual person who has a great deal to offer his employers. He is very intelligent, hard working, highly responsible, and knows how to make the most of people. His interests and talents are so broad and his drive and effort so high as to make him successful at almost anything he undertakes.

This is not to say that he performs equally well in all areas. The trick will be to find the position where the most is made of his abilities and interests. Despite his engineering training, this field would not appear to use him at his best. Everything about him, with almost no exceptions, should lead him into a top management position or a top level staff position. The top management position should be one where the line or operating aspects are subsidiary to the overall conceptualizing of the present status and trend of the business. A top level staff job might well be the one he himself describes: organization and top level planning plus management development.

He is a person who should not be forced to stand still with routine. His growth potential is great. His ceiling is high. He is a valuable employee whose future should be carefully evaluated at every major move.

COMMENTS

This report was written by the author of this manual in his capacity as psychologist with a psychological consulting firm. The purpose of the report was to analyze personality characteristics affecting the person's working career.

It illustrates the use of a topical outline with no discussion of the past. The body of the report is, of course, a description of present functioning. The recommendation implies future functioning.

I am leaving criticism of the report to the reader.

Example H

Psychological Test Report

Patient: M. K. M. Date tested:
Age: 29 Tests Administered:
Referred by: Dr. M. J. Short Form Intelligence Test
Rorschach
TAT
Sentence Completion

. . . . . .

Test Behavior

Mr. M. was at all times polite, cooperative, friendly. On even more than casual observation, his behavior and verbalizations seemed appropriate; careful scrutiny revealed strange qualities which do not appear on the surface. At various times he blocked, looked out of the window in a kind of lost state, stared at the examiner intently as if there were some kind of unspoken communication possible, showed peculiar affect.

During the Rorschach he repeatedly said that he was trying to be honest and that he hoped his reading of psychology did not affect his responses. It is true that one must probably discount some of the bizarrities (incestuous tales, etc.) on the basis of his reading and his therapy, but one cannot discount the more subtle bizarre behavior. On TAT card 3BM, he became confused and asked if he could return to it. A conversation ensued in which he said that he had not told Dr. J. everything, that there were things about himself he did not want to know, that he lived in a dream and was afraid to find it out.

Present Personality State

The patient's test responses cover a wide range of psychopathology. The test record shows autistic thinking, inappropriate affect, bizarre logic, sexual obsession, withdrawal, sexual confusion, perseveration, paranoid thoughts, probably delusional in quality, symbolic thinking, and somatic preoccupations undoubtedly delusional in nature. Of equal seriousness is his lost distance and increase of distance revealed in his taking off from a stimulus into a flight of fantasy with little reference to the stimulus, and at the same time his inability to detach himself from the "reality" of stimuli such as an inkblot.

He appears to be maintaining himself to some degree of equilibrium in his work and personal life, but this is a tenuous existence and takes a great deal out of him in terms of energy. His life reveals a growing withdrawal; he "used to" engage in sports of various kinds but now does very little except read. He "seems to move in and out of crowds" but for the past six months has gone to very few parties—"there was a time when I went out a lot." The rationalization is that he is "seeing one girl." The withdrawal, loss of contact with reality, and confused thinking are strikingly revealed in part of his self-description: "On the negative side is my psychological problem—what prevents me from doing what I think I want to do—and that is write creatively. Because I lack a, because I feel I don't really have a concept of reality, I feel I don't really have any values —so I'm sort of vacillating—deceitfully—I can and have told people things convincingly—I can be very convincing—that I absolutely do not *feel*—I feel compelled to say that."

He states openly that he drinks too much; the numerous oral references in the record lead one to conclude that the problem of alcoholism must not be taken lightly.

Dynamics

Ambivalence lies in everything he sees and does. He states, "I have a distinct feeling I'm two people," and he is. At one time he feels "six or seven years old," self-indulgent, a "beauty," dependent, to be adored, irresponsible, pampered. At other times he is a young man fast growing old, a failure, not knowing what he wants, an alcoholic, a homosexual, a weakling, and psychotic. He sees himself as talented and completely lacking in talent, a genius, an ordinary person, and "nothing," a good worker and completely disorganized, full of feeling and possessing no feeling, self-confident and completely lacking in confidence.

The world is evil, mindless, poisonous, formless, decaying, diseased, functionless, destructive; and this is the way he thinks of himself. Even things that seem good or pleasant are at the same moment evil. He is a "butterfly that has broken the chrysalis and is trying to take flight because to me it looks as evil, as mindless, as singularly destructive as the other pictures." (Rorschach Card V.)

Outside forces are impinging on him and now the smallest incident takes on significance of a symbolic and often personally threatening nature. For example, the people on Rorschach Card III are goat footed, therefore it is a Dionysian scene, therefore it is a sacrificial theme—and it is he who is being sacrificed.

He does not know what to make of people: "I'm not with it—I'm not with other people—I don't particularly like other people generally." One can seldom be sure where one stands with him: most people are "bastards," women are "all right" at one time, terribly dangerous the next. One healthy thing is that he would "like to like" people.

He is obsessed with sex. He is not sure if he is man or woman, homosexual, or a virile man's man. He believes that in sex he may prove something about himself, but the whole thing becomes confusing and in the end "sexual intercourse is empty."

He has "two diametrically opposed views of myself. I'm a hero and in my darkest depressions nothing, or at the most just an ordinary man." He is deathly afraid of being "ordinary." He "puts things off" partly because he is not functioning well enough and partly because if he actually accomplished something it might turn out to be just ordinary. This must never be proved. Even his present illness has some value to him; at least it is not ordinary. He realizes the sickness of his thinking, however, and cannot long believe his unusual thoughts are anything to be valued. In his most threatened moments he is grandiose. He has at most times "a feeling with or through your eyes that what you see isn't quite real."

Development

The genesis of his illness seems to lie in a mystifying and ambivalent relationship with his parents. The mother seems to have been an obviously destructive person to him and he can fight her. She is seen as "proud, sure, possessive, evil, prissy" with a "constrained self-pity." He identified with her to a large extent and this is undoubtedly the source of what strength he now has. He can at least handle his feelings about her obvious faults.

The father presents a different and more complex problem. He was undoubtedly very subtle in his relationships with the patient, and the patient does not know what to think or how to feel about him. He believes that the father had the seeds of greatness and that if he had succeeded, the patient's problems might not exist. His ambivalence toward his father is overwhelming. The stated desire to kill his father appears to be one of his typical intellectualizations; it would serve the purpose of erasing the problem rather than offer any kind of satisfaction of punishment or winning a duel. Liking his father would be more dangerous; this would involve some kind of responsibility to him and he fears what this might entail.

Responsibility is a central issue with many etiological implications. He feels that he should take responsibility, but as he writes on the Sentence Completion Test, "For what?" The parental upbringing seems to have been typically schizophrenogenic: he is expected to do something in order to be loved unequivocally, but he does not know what it is he is supposed to do. The parents "don't really mean what they're saying or know what they're feeling"; there is neither love nor hate coming from them. It appears that both affection and discipline were so inconsistent that he is left not knowing what to do or where to turn.

He states that after 1½ years of high school, the "bottom fell out." The examiner did not feel that it was appropriate to pursue this, but it would appear to refer to some kind of trauma which might profitably be pursued in therapy. He apparently performed adequately up to that time; after this everything was erratic.

In the past he has proved a number of times that he can do something when pressed at the last minute. Poor performances in both college and graduate school ended in his making the Dean's list in both in the *last* year.

The one thing that holds him together at this moment is his intellectualism and his hopes of writing a novel. Even here he has torturing doubts but at least he can feel at times that he is bright and that he might do something great and live in high style. If these ideas are shaken severely enough, a more obvious break with reality may be expected. He has undoubtedly contemplated suicide but the examiner does not believe that he will choose this solution. Nevertheless, his tendency to act out should not be forgotten; suicide would be an impulsive act rather than a long contemplated act. The solution would more likely be withdrawal into a completely infantile and dependent state.

Prognosis

In the face of the present disorganization, the prognosis would appear to be poor. The pathology seems to be beyond the "incipient" stage, as mentioned. There are strengths, however, and he may pull through. The course of treatment will undoubtedly be long and will require extremely careful handling to stave off a serious break with reality.

He is not unaware of other people. He has some insight into his withdrawal and does not wish to withdraw. He has potential warmth. His social skills will allow him to establish relationships; the difficulty will be in his maintaining them.

He wants therapy but is afraid of it. His therapist is probably seen as he sees everyone: good and evil; pleasant and ominous. He would like to tell all about himself but is afraid he will lose what little he has of himself. Perhaps the healthiest sign of all is his completion to the sentence: If I could let myself go, I "could really begin to do something." The trick will be to allow him to let himself go without losing his defenses with nothing to replace them.

COMMENTS

This report was written by the author of this manual. Its function was to give some additional data to a psychoanalyst about his patient.

It is quoted to illustrate a topical-chronological report, using my own preferred order—present, past, and future.

At the time of writing my two reports quoted here, I read and reread them in the guise of an imaginary supervisor and the recipients.

The best judges of these reports are the people for whom they were written, for whom they were designed to serve a useful function. The major point of this book is, after all, that reports may be written with many outlines, with many styles, with or without diagnosis, so long as they communicate clearly to the reader and meet his needs.

BIBLIOGRAPHY

Allport, G. W. *The use of personal documents in psychological science.* New York: Social Science Research Council, 1942.

American Psychiatric Association. *Diagnostic and statistical manual: mental disorders.* Washington: Author, 1952.

American Psychological Association. *Ethical standards of psychologists.* Washington: Author, 1953.

Barzun, J., & Graff, H. F. *The modern researcher.* New York: Harcourt, Brace, 1957.

Bateson, G. The convergence of science and psychiatry. In J. Ruesch & G. Bateson, *Communication: the social matrix of psychiatry.* New York: Grune & Stratton, 1951.

Bateson, G. Information and codification, a philosophical approach. In J. Ruesch & G. Bateson, *Communication: the social matrix of psychiatry.* New York: Grune & Stratton, 1951.

Beck, S. J. *Rorschach's test.* Vol. 2. *A variety of personality pictures.* New York: Grune & Stratton, 1947.

Bellak, L. *The TAT and CAT in clinical use.* New York: Grune & Stratton, 1954.

Cameron, D. E. A theory of diagnosis. In P. H. Hoch & J. Zubin (Eds.), *Current problems in psychiatric diagnosis.* New York: Grune & Stratton, 1953.

Cohen, J. A factor-analytically based rationale for the Wechsler Adult Intelligence Scale. *J. consult. Psychol.,* 1957, 21, 451–457. (a)

Cohen, J. The factorial structure of the WAIS between early adulthood and old age. *J. consult. Psychol.*, 1957, 21, 283–290. (b)

Cohen, J. The factorial structure of the WISC at ages 7–6, 10–6, and 13–6. *J. consult. Psychol.*, 1959, 23, 285–299.

Derner, G. F., & Aborn, M. *The clinical diagnosis of intelligence.* New York: Authors, 1949.

Derner, G. F., Aborn, M., & Canter, A. H. The reliability of the Wechsler-Bellevue subtests and scales. *J. consult. Psychol.*, 1950, 14, 172–179.

The editor's schnozzle, Editorial comment. *Psychiat. Quart.*, 1950, 24, 821–830.

English, H. B., & English, Ava C. *A comprehensive dictionary of psychological and psychoanalytical terms.* New York: Longmans, Green, 1958.

Evans, B., & Evans, Cornelia. *A dictionary of contemporary American usage.* New York: Random House, 1957.

Fear, R. A. *The evaluation interview.* New York: McGraw-Hill, 1958.

Ferguson, C. W. *Say it with words.* New York: Knopf, 1959.

Flesch, R. *The art of plain talk.* New York: Harper, 1946.

Foster, A. Writing psychological reports. *J. clin. Psychol.*, 1951, 7, 195.

Fowler, H. W. *A dictionary of modern English usage.* London: Oxford Univer. Press, 1950.

Fries, M. E., & Friedman, M. R. A method of organizing clinical data: a teaching aid for training residents in psychoanalytic psychotherapy. *J. Hillside Hosp.*, 1960, 9, 25–47.

Gage, N. I. Explorations in the understanding of others. *Stud. Higher Educ., Purdue Univer.*, 1951, 79, 86–96.

Garfield, S. L., Heine, R. W., & Leventhal, M. An evaluation of psychological reports in a clinical setting. *J. consult. Psychol.*, 1954, 18, 281–286.

Grayson, H. M., & Tolman, R. S. A semantic study of concepts of clinical psychologists and psychiatrists. *J. abnorm. soc. Psychol.*, 1950, 45, 216–231.

Hall, C. S., & Lindzey, G. *Theories of personality.* New York: Wiley, 1957.

Hammond, K. R., & Allen, J. M., Jr. *Writing clinical reports.* New York: Prentice-Hall, 1953.

Harrower, Molly. *Personality change and development.* New York: Grune & Stratton, 1958.

Hathaway, S. R. Clinical intuition and inferential accuracy. *J. Pers.,* 1956, 24, 223–250.

Holzberg, J. D., Alessi, S. L., & Wexler, M. Psychological case reporting at psychiatric staff conferences. *J. consult. Psychol.,* 1951, 15, 425–429.

Hunt, W. A., Wittson, C. L., & Hunt, E. B. A theoretical and practical analysis of the diagnostic process. In P. H. Hoch & J. Zubin (Eds.), *Current problems in psychiatric diagnosis.* New York: Grune & Stratton, 1953.

Klopfer, W. G. Principles of report writing. In B. Klopfer *et al., Developments in the Rorschach technique.* Vol. I. Yonkers, N.Y.: World Book Co., 1954.

Klopfer, W. G. *The psychological report.* New York: Grune & Stratton, 1960.

Leary, T. *The interpersonal diagnosis of personality.* New York: Ronald, 1957.

Lodge, G. T. How to write a psychological report. *J. clin. Psychol.,* 1953, 9, 400–402.

McClelland, D. C. *Personality.* New York: Dryden, 1951.

MacLeish, A. On the teaching of writing. *Harper's Mag.,* Oct. 1959, pp. 158–161.

Masserman, J. *Principles of dynamic psychiatry.* Philadelphia: Saunders, 1955.

Mayman, M. Style, focus, language and content of an ideal psychological test report. *J. proj. Tech.,* 1959, 23, 453–458.

Meehl, P. E., & Rosen, A. Antecedent probability and the efficiency of psychometric signs, patterns or cutting scores. *Psychol. Bull.,* 1955, 52, 194–216.

Menninger, K. A. *A manual for psychiatric case study.* New York: Grune & Stratton, 1952.

Merrill, P. W. The principles of poor writing. *Scient. Mon.,* 1947, 64, 72–74.

Morrow, R. S. The diagnostic psychological report. *Psychiat. quart. Suppl.*, 1954, 28, 102–110.

Nicholson, M. *A dictionary of American-English usage.* New York: Oxford Univer. Press, 1957.

Noyes, A. P., & Kolb, L. C. *Modern clinical psychiatry.* (5th ed.) Philadelphia: Saunders, 1958.

O. S. S. Assessment Staff. *Assessment of men.* New York: Holt, Rinehart and Winston, Inc., 1948.

Phillips, L., & Smith, J. G. *Rorschach interpretation: advanced technique.* New York: Grune & Stratton, 1953.

Plaut, A. Some psychological undercurrents of scientific and medical writing. *Scient. Mon.*, 1950, 71, 294–297.

Rackow, L. L., *et al.* A group method for the rapid screening of chronic psychiatric patients. *Amer. J. Psychiat.*, 1953, 109, 561–566.

Robinson, J. T., & Cohen, L. D. Individual bias in psychological reports. *J. clin. Psychol.*, 1954, 10, 333–336.

Ruesch, J. Communication and human relations: an interdisciplinary approach. In J. Ruesch & G. Bateson, *Communication: the social matrix of psychiatry.* New York: Grune & Stratton, 1951.

Sargent, H. Psychological test reporting: an experiment in communication. *Bull. Menninger Clin.*, 1951, 15, 175–186.

Schafer, R. *The clinical application of psychological tests.* New York: International Universities Press, 1948. (Menninger Foundation Monograph Series No. 6)

Schafer, R. *Psychoanalytic interpretation in Rorschach testing.* New York: Grune & Stratton, 1954.

Scott, P. D. Psychiatric reports for magistrate's courts. *Brit. J. Delinqu.*, 1953, 4, 82–97.

Stevens, N. E. The moral obligation to be intelligible. *Scient. Mon.*, 1950, 70, 111–115.

Strecker, E., Ebaugh, F., & Ewalt, J. *Practical clinical psychiatry.* New York: Blakiston, 1947.

Strunk, W., Jr., and White, E. B. *The elements of style.* New York: Macmillan, 1959.

Sullivan, H. S. *The psychiatric interview.* New York: Norton, 1954.

Sundberg, N. D. The acceptability of "fake" versus "bona fide" personality test interpretation. *J. abnorm. soc. Psychol.*, 1955, 50, 145–147.

Tallent, N. On individualizing the psychologist's clinical evaluation. *J. clin. Psychol.*, 1958, 14, 243–245.

Tallent, N., & Reiss, W. J. Multidisciplinary views on the preparation of written clinical psychological reports. I. Spontaneous suggestions for content. *J. clin. Psychol.*, 1959, 15, 218–221.

Taylor, J. L., & Teicher, A. A clinical approach to reporting psychological test data. *J. clin. Psychol.*, 1946, 2, 323–332.

Teicher, A. A clinical approach to reporting. In R. Watson (Ed.), *Readings in the clinical method in psychology.* New York: Harper, 1949.

Thorne, F. C. A new outline for psychological report writing. *J. clin. Psychol.*, 1956, 12, 115–122.

Ullman, L. P., Berkman, V. C., & Hamister, R. C. Psychological reports related to behavior and benefit of placement in home care. *J. clin. Psychol.*, 1958, 14, 254–259.

Wolberg, L. R. *The technique of psychotherapy.* New York: Grune & Stratton, 1954.

Young, L. Diagnosis as a creative process. *Soc. Casewk*, 1956, 37, 275–280.

INDEX

68 69 70   7 6 5 4 3 2 1